Writing this book has only been possible because of the support from family, friends, experts in their field, and an amazing group of women who have shared their experiences. Thank you to all.

Project Editor – Jo Ebdon-Muir
Editor – Joanna Clements
Editor – Jenny Carson
Editor/Pharmacist – Ryan Benbow
Publishing Director – Cheryl Thallon

First published in 2022
by Leeds & London Partnership
15-17 High March, Daventry, Northants NN11 4HB, UK

A CIP catalogue record of this book is available from the British Library
ISBN 978-1-7391378-0-9

The information in this book is designed to be advisory and helpful. It is not intended to treat or diagnose any medical conditions and is not a substitute for professional medical advice. Please consult your GP before starting, changing or stopping any medical treatment. The author and publisher are not responsible for any liability arising directly or indirectly from the use or misuse of the information contained in this book.

Printed in the UK on FSC certified paper

The *Menopause* Journal

AIMÉE BENBOW
BSc (Hons), MSc, ANutr

FOREWORD BY DR SIOBHAN BRENNAN

Foreword by Dr Siobhan Brennan

My menopause journey was not a traditional one being thrust into a surgically-induced menopause at the age of 39, but I was determined not to let this define me.

I started running at the age of 40, to help me manage the impact of this premature menopause. I've committed to healthy eating and see a clear correlation between diet and wellbeing for me and my patients. Supplements and complementary medicines that have a clear evidence base can add to this. How I eat has evolved as I've developed my understanding of the hormonal changes that impact my body metabolism.

Traditionally talked about in hushed tones that conjure emotive images of women losing their mind, no longer being fertile and dripping in uncomfortable hot sweats, it had been almost normalised to feel rotten for many women through the perimenopause and menopause, when your periods finally stop.

While it is an expected, normal physiological event for most women, this doesn't mean that the decrease in our hormone levels during the menopause is an easy transition or lacking in impact. The perimenopause is the phase before this, when periods become erratic as hormonal levels start to fall.

Its impact can be variable in that some women seem to breeze through without any symptoms other than their periods stopping but others are profoundly impacted by the diverse and variable symptoms that can affect so many bodily systems.

Remember though, whilst you may feel your symptoms are attributable to the menopause, allow your GP to unpick these symptoms and make sure nothing else is going on. It's very easy to put everything down to the menopause but it can mimic other conditions, so it's sensible to speak with your health practitioner.

Whilst there are expected timeframes that doctors expect this to happen in, it is important to remember that your journey may not fit traditional timeframes. Perimenopause and the Menopause is a journey that is individual to you.

As women, we are often defined by our hormones from periods to childbirth to menopause. Our hormonal fluctuations have been accepted and normalised for many years without any true understanding of their impact on woman's emotional and physical performance.

The negative impact of hormones is only now being talked about in sport, life and work.

The wide range of menopause symptoms can and have been attributed to the ageing process, depression, anxiety, hysteria, fibromyalgia and so on. The training of doctors historically has been minimal around the menopause but this has changed over the last few years, with a push in education and willingness of GPs to learn more about this topic of female health.

It is not all about HRT medication when managing the menopause. The most supportive management includes self-care, being mindful of our emotions, investing in what we eat and when we eat. The role of exercise is paramount to help manage symptoms but also assists in bone maintenance and muscle density, which decreases in the menopause.

Careful consideration of the benefits of complementary therapies and supplements that can help treat the impact of symptoms all play a pivotal role too. It is important to consider that whether or not a woman chooses or is suitable for HRT, the foundations of managing the menopause lie in a healthy wholesome diet and lifestyle that acknowledge our changes in metabolism. What we eat, how we exercise, which complementary medicines and supplements we choose all impact on our health outcomes. Above all else, we have a responsibility to invest in ourselves long-term, in a truly holistic fashion.

I know many brilliant women that have not been defined by the negative impact of the menopause, but been empowered by it. Let's all embrace the menopause armed with knowledge and ownership of our bodies.

This is where The Menopause Journal comes into its own.

GPs, like myself, are busier than ever and may only have 10 minutes per appointment, so having a documented symptom-checker is useful both for you and your doctor to understand the true impact of the menopause and quantify your specific array symptoms on your life.

The data provided in The Menopause Journal allows you to get the most out of a consultation with any health professional. Keeping a journal helps you truly understand how you feel now, but also, to reflect on how far you have come in dealing with the challenges you face.

The design has been formatted to make it straightforward to check in and out so you don't feel overwhelmed to even start.

Ownership of our personal menopause journey is paramount. Use this journal to invest in yourself and celebrate your successes.

Wishing you exceptional health and happiness.

Siobhan Brennan

General Practitioner

"So many women I've talked to see menopause as an ending. But I've discovered

this is your moment

to reinvent yourself after years of focusing on the needs of everyone else. It's your opportunity to get clear about what matters to you and then to pursue that with all of your energy, time and talent."

Oprah Winfrey

Introduction

Not yet in my 40s, you may wonder why I have written this book about the menopause. Having witnessed the trauma of the 'change-of-life' in my close family and in my professional life, I decided to create a tool that would enable me to manage my own transition – and help many others experience their menopause, their way.

You hold in your hands the result of my research, based on the experiences of countless people who have described their menopause symptoms and experiences, and helped me write this practical workbook, The Menopause Journal.

My name is Aimée Benbow and I'm a qualified Nutritionist with a BSc in Nutrition (2008) and an MSc in Nutritional Medicine (2018). Professionally, I am Head of Technical Services at a leading food supplement company. My day-to-day role includes research into the latest innovations in human health, nutrition and lifestyle.

In my research, exploring the causes, symptoms and experiences of the menopause, I've observed that it is perceived very differently between people and also by different cultures. Did you know, for example, in some Eastern cultures this time of a woman's life is viewed as a positive, liberating phase, whereas in the West, we historically have felt judged by our sudden inability to reproduce. Not only can the menopause be viewed differently between people and cultures, the transition itself can be experienced very differently between individuals. Some may sail through, while others face major symptoms which significantly impact their quality of life.

Page-by-page, this fully referenced Menopause Journal gives you the power to take control - tracking your daily symptoms, diet and lifestyle. With daily journalling, you will get to grips with your physical and emotional symptoms, understand how your diet and lifestyle choices impact on your symptoms, then get the right advice to pin down a daily routine ensuring you get your menopause, your way.

The next 90 days will be life-changing – for you and everyone around you
– embrace the change!

BSc (Hons) MSc ANutr

What happens during the menopause?

Simply, the menopause is defined as the time in a woman's life when menstruation stops. In reality, there is so much more to this stage of life. It's a natural phase which can be a signal of freedom but whilst it's natural and normal, it can be daunting and unexpected. Understandably, this can be a very emotional time and many women often feel unprepared for the challenges ahead.

In the UK, the average age for menopause is 51, however the majority of women are likely to experience the menopause transition between the ages of 45 and 55 [1]. There are over 40 different symptoms associated with the menopause and research shows that over 80% of women will experience menopausal symptoms of varying intensities [2]. This journal will guide you through what happens during the menopause, the different stages and potential symptoms, as well as how to manage them and support your body for long term health – through the menopause and beyond.

The perimenopause is the beginning part of your journey. This is the transition phase when hormone levels decline, specifically the production of oestrogen and progesterone, which causes irregular cycles. Contrary to belief, it is often the perimenopause phase that causes many of the well-known symptoms rather than the menopause itself. This stage can start up to 10 years before entering the postmenopause phase.

When no cycles have occurred in over 12 months, this is then considered as the postmenopause stage. At this time the severity of symptoms lessens but can still be experienced to varying degrees for some years after.

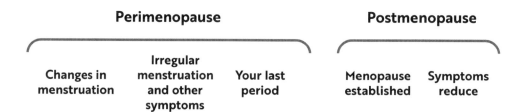

Perimenopause

Changes in menstruation | Irregular menstruation and other symptoms | Your last period

Postmenopause

Menopause established | Symptoms reduce

So how do I know if I am going through the perimenopause?

The perimenopause can normally be identified by your doctor, either through listening to your description of symptoms you are experiencing and taking into consideration your age, or it can be confirmed through blood tests measuring hormone levels. Sometimes the symptoms can be attributed to other things which is why keeping a close record of what you are experiencing is helpful.

Am I on a hormonal rollercoaster?

During the perimenopause there is a significant decline in specific hormones, in particular oestrogen and progesterone. Let's look at the different sex hormones produced by the body and the role they play:

Oestrogen – This is the leading female sex hormone and while both men and women produce this hormone it is far more dominant in the female body. This hormone is responsible for female body development during puberty as well as the regulation of the reproductive system, specifically the menstruation cycle. Oestrogen is mainly produced by the ovaries but is also produced in small amounts by the adrenal glands and fat cells. These become the main oestrogen production sites once menopause occurs. Internal levels of oestrogen fluctuate during the menstrual cycle in order to stimulate the release of eggs from the ovaries. The sudden drop in oestrogen levels is the main culprit for inducing menopausal symptoms.

Progesterone – is a steroid hormone which is also produced by the ovaries in the second half of the menstrual cycle in order to prepare the body for pregnancy. Abnormal production of progesterone by the body can cause tender breast tissue and impact mood. It can also have a significant impact on the frequency and heaviness of the menstrual cycle and low levels are often implicated with infertility. The decline in progesterone levels during the perimenopause is one of the key factors why menstrual bleeds begin to cease.

Testosterone – often referred to as the 'male' sex hormone, testosterone is still produced in the female body by the adrenal glands and in small amounts in the ovaries. This hormone in women is needed for libido, muscle strength and bone mass. During the menopause naturally occurring levels of testosterone have been shown to decrease.

Understanding common symptoms

Hot sweats? Palpitations? Low mood? Is this all normal?

The sudden decline in the body's production of oestrogen and progesterone initiates the perimenopause phase and what follows this can often be a wide range of a varying symptoms from mild to life changing, and it can impact women in many ways. For some, the symptoms are more physical and in others, psychological and cognitive symptoms are more of a challenge. We will now talk through some of the common symptoms associated with the menopause and gain a better understanding of the cause. There may be additional symptoms you experience that are not listed below, please refer to the symptom list on page 39.

Hot flushes and night sweats – these are both linked to the body's lowered ability to regulate temperature, which is associated with a reduction in the function of the hypothalamus. The hypothalamus is located in the brain and plays a role in the regulation of hormones as well as body's core temperature regulation. The onset of night sweats may significantly impact **sleep** and insomnia is a symptom of menopause reported by up to 40% of women [3].

Hormone headaches or migraine - can be a result of sharp fluctuations in hormones. Even prior to menopause, women may notice a link between menstruation and headache or migraine occurrence, and this can be magnified during the menopause.

Low mood and anxiety - Irritability, depression and anxiety are frequent menopausal symptoms. As oestrogen declines it allows the stress hormone, known as cortisol, to rise and so the ability to cope with stress decreases along with an increase in feelings of fatigue. Serotonin is the neurotransmitter that produces feelings of wellbeing, however, as oestrogen declines, serotonin production decreases and the number of serotonin receptors in the brain declines. This in turn increases the risk of lowered mood and depression [4].

Thinning hair - Oestrogen plays a regulatory role in hair growth and hair loss. During the reproductive years the rate of growth and loss are balanced however as oestrogen declines during menopause the balance changes to a greater loss than growth phase which can result in thinning hair.

Tissue strength and structure – As well as playing a role in hair growth, oestrogen is also involved in collagen production. Reduced oestrogen production during menopause can lead to the development of facial fine lines and wrinkles. This same reduction in collagen production can also be a causal factor for **vaginal dryness**, as the supportive tissue within this area becomes thinner, less flexible and drier.

The loss of tissue strength can have a negative impact on the bladder causing **bladder weakness**. This means women struggle to hold onto urine for any length of time and is referred to as incontinence. This is seen predominately in postmenopausal women, and it is reported that up to 50% of postmenopausal women suffer from incontinence [5].

Brain fog - As many as 60% of menopausal women have identified difficulties with concentrating and other issues surrounding cognition. The fluctuation in hormone levels again has a role to play in these cognitive issues as hormones improve neuron communication and growth of neural cells. Additionally vasomotor (blood flow) symptoms of menopause are believed to play a role in the development of brain fog [6].

Low libido – As well as oestrogen and progesterone production declining during the menopause, testosterone also decreases which is an important factor in libido. This coupled with vaginal dryness can have a huge impact on sex drive at this time.

Joint pain – Many women report that their joints become stiff and painful over these transitional years. This can be an indicator of reduced collagen and tissue production, therefore leading to lack of support to the joints through reduced levels of connective tissue and cartilage. Non-clinical data supports this theory although the exact link and cause between reduced oestrogen levels and joint pain has not been determined [7].

Weight re-distribution – Weight gain is a common problem linked to menopause and this is mainly due to fat re-distribution particularly around the abdomen. This happens because the normal balance between oestrogen and testosterone in the female body is disrupted leading to a higher testosterone to oestrogen ratio, and this imbalance promotes the accumulation of abdominal fat [8]. The reduction in muscle mass noted with age has a compound effect as this is directly linked to a reduced metabolism, which in turn leads to weight gain [9].

Cardiovascular disease risk - the risk and prevalence of metabolic syndrome increases during menopause [10]. Metabolic syndrome includes risk factors such as central obesity, insulin resistance (pre-diabetes) and hypertension (high blood pressure). These in turn all lead to an increased risk of cardiovascular disease in women later in life [11].

Additionally, when oestrogen levels decline, the balance between LDL (bad cholesterol) and HDL (beneficial cholesterol) changes, leading to increased levels of bad cholesterol. This higher level of LDL cholesterol gives rise to an increased risk of oxidised LDL cholesterol which is known to be detrimental to heart health through the increased risk of atherosclerosis.

Reduced bone density - the reduced level of oestrogen is associated with reduced bone density and in turn significantly increases the risk of osteoporosis. Losing bone mass is a normal part of the ageing process, however the first few years of the menopause causes women to lose bone mass much faster which can result in an increased risk of bone breakages [12].

Prescription medication for menopause symptoms

What can my GP do for me?

Doctors can prescribe medication to help with the common symptoms of menopause known as 'Hormone Replacement Therapy' or 'HRT'. This provides the body with the hormones it is no longer making to reduce the severity of the symptoms. However, there can be several reasons women do not opt to take this medication:

· They may be medically advised not to
· They may not tolerate taking hormones
· They wish to try a more natural approach

In addition, some women suffer with various side effects from taking hormone replacement therapy including breast swelling or tenderness, nausea, cramps, digestive discomfort and headaches. In some forms of HRT there is a link to an increased risk of blood clots [13] and breast cancer [14]. Therefore, women with a history of oestrogen dominant cancers or who have a genetic risk factor for breast cancer are not advised to take HRT. It is also not recommended for those with uncontrolled hypertension, severe liver disease and those with a history of blood clots.

However, there are also numerous benefits to taking HRT, as well aiding with some of the common menopause symptoms, there is good evidence that it can prevent osteoporosis [15] and in some cases, cardiovascular disease (CVD). Outcomes on the prevention of CVD are variable and may depend on dosage, timing and route of administration [16]. HRT is available in many different forms including an oral tablet, hormone gels, patches and creams. Vaginal pessaries can also be prescribed which specifically help with vaginal dryness.

Alongside HRT, other medications to help manage symptoms are available. For example, clonidine is a non-hormonal medication sometimes prescribed to assist with blood pressure and headaches but has also shown to be beneficial for reducing hot flushes [17].

Other medication commonly offered by medical practitioners includes anti-depressants to alleviate feelings of low mood and depressive symptoms. Frequent side effects from this type of medication include nausea, increased feelings of anxiousness, loss of appetite, indigestion, headaches, reduced libido and sweating. However, a study found that selective serotonin reuptake inhibitors (SSRIs), which are a type of anti-depressant, helped reduce the number of hot flushes experienced by those in peri and early postmenopause [18].

Non-steroidal anti-inflammatories (NSAIDs) can be used to offset the pain associated with inflamed and painful joints. These include over the counter medications such as aspirin and ibuprofen. These work by blocking a specific enzyme in the body used to make prostaglandins, which are required to trigger an inflammatory reaction. Blocking this enzyme, and hence the production of prostaglandins, therefore creates an anti-inflammatory effect. However, this group of medication is not without issues, as those taking NSAIDs often report digestive complaints such as indigestion and in severe cases ulcers, headaches, dizziness and drowsiness.

Selective Oestrogen Receptor Modulators (SERMs), such as raloxifene and bazedoxifene, can be prescribed for osteoporosis or reduced bone density related to menopause. This class of drugs work by having a similar effect to the hormone oestrogen to protect bone density. Unfortunately, the side effects of this medication can include hot flushes, blood clots and leg cramps.

If cardiovascular risk factors become apparent, such as hypertension and increased cholesterol levels, the conventional route usually relies upon blood pressure lowering drugs such as diuretic medication, ACE inhibitors and calcium channel blockers and for cholesterol, statins. Although these drugs are important in clinical practice to help reduce the risk of serious cardiovascular events taking place, some individuals can experience side effects with these, particularly with statins.

Statins work by reducing cholesterol levels in the body, however, they are not able to determine between HDL and LDL and instead work to simply reduce total cholesterol levels. This can be problematic because cholesterol plays a critical role in the body as it is required for cell structure, hormone production and the conversion of sunlight into vitamin D. So, we can see if cholesterol levels drop too low, it can impact other areas of health. Statin use has also been linked to fatigue and reduced energy levels, interestingly this appears to be more common in women than men and can have a big impact on quality of life [19]. However, this type of medication is equally important in reducing total cardiovascular disease risk.

We have looked at the medical options and what may be offered to you if you visit your GP to discuss your symptoms. You may also get advice on medical options from specialised health practitioners who have trained and studied the menopause. You can find your nearest through the British Menopause Society https://thebms.org.uk/find-a-menopause-specialist/.

Now let's take a look at the role a balanced diet and lifestyle can have on this time of life.

Foundations of your menopause diet

How can food help?

We hear about diet and lifestyle a lot when we talk about health, but can they really make that much difference? It's time for us to look at the evidence.

Achieving the right foundations of nutrition is critical to making sure your body is in the best possible position to face this milestone. Throughout our life stages it's important to get the essential nutrients at the appropriate amounts to avoid disease and chronic conditions and a balanced diet can allow you to live a fulfilled life with abundant health and energy. This is especially true for those going through menopause whereby getting the balance of diet and lifestyle right can have a huge impact on how the transition affects them. In this journal you can keep a log of what you have eaten each day so you can look back and see if you are consuming a well-balanced diet.

Good nutrition requires carefully considering both the macro nutrients (fats, proteins and carbohydrates) and the micronutrients (essential vitamins and minerals). As well as making sure we get these vital nutrients daily, it's also important to consider the food source. You may have heard of the term 'wholefoods' or 'unprocessed foods', these terms refer to foods in their most natural state and have not undergone any form of processing. You will be able to identify these by the way they are packaged, and the number of ingredients listed. A wholefood would generally be considered as a food that contains a single ingredient, free from additives and preservatives. It is advisable to choose organic produce where possible to avoid the presence and use of artificial fertilisers and pesticides on the final product.

As well as opting for wholefoods, we should also try to incorporate a wide variety of colourful foods into our daily routine, this way, it ensures we are consuming a good range of nutrients with each meal and therefore unlikely to be deficient or sub-optimal in any of the key nutrients needed.

The Mediterranean diet is largely hailed as being one of the healthiest diets for longevity and quality of life and there is good research to back this popular opinion [20]. The Mediterranean diet encourages a good intake of fruits and vegetables, healthy fats such as olive oil and omega-3 as well as unrefined and unprocessed carbohydrates which are rich in fibre. Interestingly, the Mediterranean diet has been studied specifically in menopausal women with findings to suggest that those who adhered to the diet experienced reduced vasomotor symptoms (hot flushes and night sweats) [21]. This traditional diet was studied in peri and postmenopausal women and found those following this diet were negatively associated with weight gain and obesity compared to those not following the diet [22].

So, what does a well-balanced meal look like? The diagram below demonstrates what a healthy meal looks like in terms of macronutrient breakdown. By increasing the fruit and vegetable portion of the plate, you will naturally increase the micronutrient level of the meal as well.

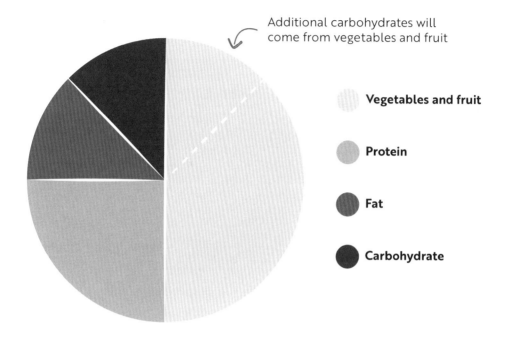

Additional carbohydrates will come from vegetables and fruit

Vegetables and fruit

Protein

Fat

Carbohydrate

Phytoestrogens

A balanced diet is important for everyone, regardless of their stage of life. However, there is a useful tool for those going through menopause in the form of a group of foods known as phytoestrogens.

Dietary phytoestrogens are foods containing compounds which have oestrogen mimicking effects on the body and work on receptors to allow the body to think there is oestrogen present. As they possess oestrogen like activity, they can assist in reducing the severity of menopausal symptoms without some of the risks associated with taking HRT [23]. They have been shown to be effective for common symptoms such as hot flushes and night sweats, also they are able to reduce the risk of more serious factors associated with the menopause such as breast cancer [24]. This occurs because phytoestrogens work differently depending on what tissue they are acting. For example, they will have an anti-oestrogenic effect in breast tissue but often an oestrogenic effect on bones. Phytoestrogens specifically activate beta oestrogen receptors and not alpha receptors, and it is the activation of alpha receptors in breast tissue which is linked to increased cancer risk [25].

Isoflavones and lignans are common forms of phytoestrogens found in food. Isoflavones are found in foods such as soya, legumes, lentils and the herb red clover. Lignans are found in seeds especially flaxseeds, wholegrains and vegetables. The table highlights a list of the common foods isoflavones and lignans can be found in [26]:

Food sources high in Isoflavones (from high to low)	Food sources high in Lignans (from high to low)
Soy	Flaxseed
Soy protein	Carrot
Soy sprouts	Cabbage
Miso	Lentils
Tofu	Cauliflower
Soy cheese	Onion
Soy milk	Garlic
Soy sauce	Soybean
Mung beans	Strawberry
Lentils	Cucumber
Peas	Potato
Kidney beans	Tomato
Tea	Banana
Currants	Cashew
Barley	Apple
Coconut	Orange
	Black eyed peas
	Peanut
	Walnut
	Mung bean
	Mango

Dietary intake of foods containing phytoestrogens varies between different countries. In Asia the average intake is between 15-50mg daily, while in the West it is only approximately 2mg per day [27]. Interestingly, research has uncovered that woman in Asia report much fewer menopausal symptoms and with lower severity, suggesting the high consumption of soya could play a role [28]. While there is no recommended daily intake for phytoestrogens, aiming to increase your intake can prove helpful in reducing the severity of symptoms.

Antioxidants

Antioxidants in the diet are crucial at every stage in life but are of particular importance during menopause. Antioxidants are substances that may prevent or delay cell damage within the body. They work by neutralising unstable atoms known as 'free radicals' that are naturally produced by the body when our cells make energy. These free radicals can cause damage to cells in the body, known as 'oxidative damage' which long term can lead to conditions such as joint degeneration and cardiovascular disease.

Certain dietary and lifestyle factors such as smoking and environmental pollution can accelerate the production of free radicals. As our bodies age, its own production of antioxidants declines, therefore obtaining these from the diet becomes even more important.

Oestrogen has been shown to have antioxidant properties, therefore the decline in this hormone during menopause, alongside reduced natural antioxidant production, creates even higher levels of oxidative damage to the body [29].

You have probably heard of some of the most common antioxidants before – vitamin C, vitamin E and beta carotene, for example, are all familiar nutrients when it comes to healthy eating. Other antioxidants found in wholefoods include selenium, zinc and polyphenols, and the more variety we eat, the stronger our defences become.

Exciting research has shown that women whose diet included more antioxidants were less likely to experience menopausal symptoms such as hot flushes, anxiety, and brain fog [30]. The list on the following page shows some examples of antioxidant rich foods that are ideal to incorporate into your daily meals for an antioxidant boost. Note how many are red or purple, suggesting natural foods of this colour are often high in antioxidants. The total antioxidant activity of each food is measured as oxygen radical absorbance capacity (ORAC) which is essentially how effective it is at neutralising free radicals.

Note that cooking fruit and vegetables can damage many of the antioxidants or reduce their activity, therefore where possible opt for eating these raw or only very lightly steamed. Although there is no recommended intake of antioxidants, aim to include as many foods rich in antioxidants into each of your meals.

Food Type	Typical serving (g)	ORAC units per gram	ORAC units per serving
VERY HIGH IN ANTIOXIDANTS			
Red Kidney Beans	92	144.04	13252
Pinto Bean	96	119.37	11460
Blueberry	145	61.84	8967
Artichoke	84	92.77	7793
Blackberry	144	52.45	7553
Prunes	85	83.99	7139
Dark Plums	88	73.01	6425
Strawberry	166	35.41	5878
Raspberry	123	47.65	5861
Red Apple	138	42.34	5843
Green Apple	138	38.6	5327
Cherry	145	33.44	4849
Russet potatoes	299	15.27	4566
Red Pears	166	17.38	2885
Oranges	140	17.85	2499
Raisins	82	30.02	2462
Broccoli	85	28.1	2389
Red Cabbage	75	31.46	2360
Red Grapes	160	12.6	2016

Food Type	Typical serving (g)	ORAC units per gram	ORAC units per serving
HIGH IN ANTIOXIDANTS			
Black eyed peas	52	37.07	1928
Beetroot	68	27.65	1880
Red Grapefruit	123	15.13	1861
White potato	173	10.41	1801
Green Grapes	160	11.18	1789
Yellow pepper	186	9.56	1778
Peach	98	18.13	1777
Asparagus	90	16.44	1480
Apricot	105	13.09	1374
Tangerine	84	16.13	1355
Onion	105	12.2	1281
Almonds	28	42.82	1216
Pineapple	155	7.64	1184
Red Lettuce	68	16.5	1122

Source 31

Essential fatty acids

Fats are present in all animal-derived foods and surprisingly, most vegetables also have a very small amount of fat present. Foods generally contain several forms of fat, the common fat types in our food include, saturated fat, monounsaturated fat (MUFAs), polyunsaturated fat (PUFAs), trans and hydrogenated fats. In the UK, the total dietary fat intake is recommended to not exceed 35% of our daily intake of calories, which in women is roughly 70g.

'Healthy' or 'good' fats are important to consider when looking at the overall diet. Although it was historically thought that fat intake was bad for health and simply made you gain weight, certain types of fat are essential to the body including the PUFAs omega-3 and omega-6 and these must be consumed through diet. These fats are required by the body for hormone production, to make cells, to manage inflammation and to support energy production.

Omega-3 essential fatty acids are a group of fatty acids found mainly in nuts, seeds and fish. Alpha linolenic acid (ALA) is the form found in seed oils such as flaxseed and perilla seed, and the remaining eicosapentaenoic acid (EPA), docosapentaenoic acid (DPA) and docosahexaenoic acid (DHA) are found in oily fish and algae. Research has revealed that the most potent anti-inflammatory effects are the omega-3s in the form of EPA and DHA [32]. However, consumption of seeds rich in ALA means that the body can transform the omega-3 fatty acids into the forms present in fish and algae to exert their benefits towards inflammation and cell structure.

In terms of the menopause, several scientific studies have demonstrated encouraging results between omega-3 intake and reduced symptoms. A study reviewing EPA and DHA supplementation in menopausal transition for major depressive disorder found a significant decrease in both depressive measures and the number of hot flushes experienced per day [33]. Elsewhere, it has been demonstrated that the anti-inflammatory action of omega-3 fatty acids has been linked to reduced joint pain and inflammation, making foods containing omega-3 a good natural treatment option for those suffering from inflamed joint conditions [34].

Further research has also shown that dietary intake of EPA and DHA was significantly associated with a reduced risk of coronary heart disease, [35] which is an increased threat in post-menopausal individuals.

Omega-6 fatty acids include linoleic acid which is a polyunsaturated essential fatty acid, found abundantly in the Western diet in sources such as vegetable oils, corn oil, nuts and avocados. There are important roles within the body that omega-6 essential fatty acids fulfil, for example arachidonic acid, another form of omega-6, is involved in the production of brain cells, and gamma-linolenic acid (GLA) has been researched for hormone and skin health. Therefore, inclusion in the diet is important but aim to look for healthier sources of omega-6 essential fatty acids such as hemp seed, avocado and evening primrose oil.

The research investigating the effects of omega-6 essential fatty acids on health are conflicting. An omega-6 dominant diet has been associated with excessive inflammation that caused tissue damage and increased the risk of diseases, obesity and the worsening of inflammatory conditions such as arthritis. On the other hand, high levels of GLA as found in evening primrose oil, have demonstrated beneficial and anti-inflammatory effects on inflamed skin conditions such as atopic dermatitis [36]. Evening primrose oil has also been studied for hot flushes relating to menopause. Six weeks after consuming 1g of evening primrose oil daily led to significant improvements in the intensity of the hot flushes [37].

Considered as an important marker of healthy fat consumption, the omega-6:3 ratio was first discussed in research in relation to the traditional Mediterranean diet. Typically, it is considered that the Western diet omega-6:3 ratio can be as high as 20:1, but the goal is to reduce the ratio to 3:1. It is at the lower ratio that the prevention and management of chronic health conditions can be achieved.

Healthy eating guidelines in the UK advise we eat two portions of fish (2 x 140g) a week, at least one of which should be an oily type (e.g. salmon, sardines, trout, or mackerel), to help improve our omega-3 fatty acid intake and omega-6:3 ratio. If you are vegetarian or vegan, ensure you get a good intake of omega-3 through seeds and nuts and consider an algae EPA and DHA supplement.

There are two further omega fatty acids, **omega-7**, palmitoleic acid and **omega-9**, oleic acid. Both can be made in the body but there are also some dietary sources. Sea buckthorn, avocado, olives and macadamia nuts are the main omega-7 food sources. Omega-9 fatty acids are widely spread throughout vegetable and animal products. Rich sources include olives, avocado, sunflower seeds, hazelnuts and almonds. Research suggests that omega-9 is useful for heart health by promoting HDL-cholesterol and decreasing LDL-cholesterol.

Saturated fats are found predominantly in animal meats and can be identified as the oil which leaches out of the meat while cooking, and re-solidifies again at room temperature. Other examples include cheese, coconut oil and butter. Saturated fat is transformed into cholesterol, which is used to produce hormones. Therefore, it is important to contain small levels within the everyday diet to ensure the body has the building blocks to continue making hormones such as oestrogen. However, too much saturated fat has been associated with elevated cholesterol which in turn puts the cardiovascular system at risk. Aim to consume this form of fat in moderation, no more than 20g daily.

Hydrogenated and trans fats are known to have a negative impact on health and are best avoided. These types of fats can be produced when fragile fats are heated, which occurs when seed fats are used for high temperature cooking. Trans fats in the diet are directly associated with numerous health implications including cardiovascular heart disease and stroke [38]. Due to this risk, Public Health England recommend that total trans-fat intake does not exceed 2% of total energy intake. These types of fats are more likely to be found in highly processed foods, therefore check the label to avoid those foods using hydrogenated fats and oils.

Carbohydrates

Carbohydrates are an important part of our diet as they are an easy energy source for us. Like fats, there are different types of carbohydrates, some of which are more beneficial to the human body than others. These can be consumed either as starches or sugars. Unrefined, starchy carbohydrates are considered the healthier option as these usually contain a good amount of fibre. These complex carbohydrates are found in foods such as vegetables, brown rice, sweet potatoes and wholewheat flour. They are beneficial for the digestive system and can assist with some of the digestive complaints, weight gain and cardiovascular risks linked to menopause [39]. Fibre is beneficial to the friendly bacteria in our gut which ensures a healthy digestive system, and also plays a role in maintaining metabolic health [40]. Additionally, a good intake of fibre alongside adequate water consumption, helps relieve constipation which is common during menopause.

It is worth being aware that high fibre intake is associated with reduced circulating oestrogen levels [41], due to a decreased re-absorption of oestrogen by the colon. Therefore consuming phytoestrogenic foods is strongly recommended when consuming a high fibre diet. Researchers in the field of oncology have noted the benefits of fibre consumption in significantly reducing the risk of breast cancer in postmenopausal women [42].

Whereas complex, unrefined, starchy carbohydrates digest slowly, those which have been refined and heavily processed tend to contain simple sugars that cause glucose to spike in our blood more quickly. Examples of foods which contain carbohydrates in the form of sugars include biscuits, cakes, fruit juice, sugar laden breakfast cereals, white bread and white rice.

As these types of carbohydrates cause blood glucose spikes, long term consumption can significantly increase the chances of type 2 diabetes [43], heart disease and obesity.

As well as the long-term effects of a high sugar consumption, sugar spikes on daily basis cause a rise and fall of both mood and energy levels throughout the day. Therefore, we can aim to reduce the side effects of a high sugar diet by opting for more starchy carbs, which release sugar much slower and therefore sustains energy levels for longer.

The UK government advises 260 grams of total carbohydrate per day, making up 50% of our total diet. Some of this will come from vegetables, particularly fruits and starchy roots. In addition, aim for a portion of unrefined carbohydrate the size of your fist as an appropriate amount to have at mealtimes. This could be cooked brown rice, cooked wholemeal pasta or wholemeal bread as examples . A daily maximum limit of 30g of refined simple carbohydrate or sugar rich food and drink is recommended. This equates to seven teaspoons of sugar.

Complex Carbohydrates	Simple Carbohydrates
Whole grains	Chips and crisps
Brown rice	Sweets
Wholewheat pasta	Chocolate
Brown bread	Energy / fizzy drinks
Fruits and vegetables	Pastries and biscuits
Sweet potatoes	White bread

Protein

Protein is an essential building block for the body and is needed for growth and repair of muscle and tissue health. This is of particular interest during the menopause as we know that tissue health declines due to reduced collagen production. Sarcopenia (muscle wastage) is also a known risk in post-menopausal individuals [44], and therefore ensuring sufficient protein intake from the diet can help minimise this. It is suggested that woman over 50 should be looking to increase protein intake above the recommended intake of 0.8g of protein per kg of body weight to 1.1g of protein per kg of body weight daily [45]. For example a 70kg woman would need 77g of protein daily. To put this into perspective a salmon fillet provides approx. 20-25g and a beef steak approx. 30-40g of protein.

As mentioned previously, bone health can be a concern during the menopause as reduced oestrogen during this time leads to increased bone loss, making bones more brittle. Previously, it was suggested that high protein intake was detrimental to bone health and density, however, a review paper conducted by the National Osteoporosis Foundation concluded that most studies found a positive influence of protein intake on bone health [46].

Protein also has an important role on regulating the immune system which is key to good health as we age.

The main food sources in the diet for protein are meat, dairy, nuts and grains. Protein is consumed through the diet in the form of amino acids. Some amino acids can be produced by the body from the combination of others, whereas some are deemed as 'essential' because they can only be obtained from food. Therefore, it is important to obtain protein through different food sources to ensure an adequate intake of the essential amino acids.

The table below shows some of the most protein rich foods [47].

Food type	Protein content (g) per 100g	Food type	Protein content (g) per 100g
Animal sources of protein		Cottage cheese	9.4
Meat		Plain Greek-style yogurt	5.7
Chicken breast (grilled, no skin)	32.0	Plain low-fat yogurt	4.8
Pork chop (lean, grilled)	31.6		
Beef steak (lean, grilled)	31.0	**Plant sources of protein**	
Lamb chop (lean, grilled)	29.2	**Pulses**	
Fish		Red lentils (boiled)	7.6
Tuna (canned in brine)	24.9	Chickpeas (canned)	7.2
Salmon (grilled)	24.6	**Beans**	
Cod (baked)	23.9	Tofu (steamed)	8.1
Mackerel (grilled)	20.3	Kidney beans (canned)	6.9
Seafood		Baked beans	5.0
Crab (canned in brine)	18.1	**Grains**	
Mussels (cooked)	17.7	Wheat flour (brown)	12.2
Prawns (cooked)	15.4	Rice (easy cook, boiled)	10.9
Eggs		Bread (brown)	7.9
Chicken egg (whole, boiled)	14.1	Bread (white)	7.9
Dairy		Pasta (dried cooked)	4.8
Whole milk	3.4	Porridge oats	3.0
Semi-skimmed milk	3.5	**Nuts**	
Skimmed milk	3.5	Almonds	21.1
Cheddar cheese	25.4	Walnuts	14.7
Reduced-fat cheddar	27.9	Hazelnuts	14.1

Meal and recipe tips

Some of the below ideas might help you add more key nutrients and phytoestrogenic foods to your diet

- Add flaxseeds into morning cereal to increase phytoestrogen intake in the form of lignans.

- Swap cow's milk for soya milk for added phytoestrogens in the form of isoflavones.

- Add fruits such as blueberries, strawberries and raspberries to cereal for added antioxidants.

- Consider high protein snacks such as boiled eggs or nuts and seeds to get added protein and omega-3.

- Swap out margarine or butter high in saturated fat for cashew nut butter or a nutritious mashed avocado spread.

- Liven up your salad with the use of cold pressed plant oils such as sesame, flax or olive oil

- Add lentils to soups for increased phytoestrogen content.

- Add beans, such as kidney beans, to salads and main meals for added protein and phytoestrogen content.

- For a snack, consider carrot sticks and houmous. Carrot sticks are high in the antioxidant beta-carotene and houmous is made from chickpeas which are rich in protein.

- Want something sweet? Opt for dark chocolate, high in cacao content which acts as a strong antioxidant.

In this section of the journal, we have reviewed the evidence supporting why a healthy and balanced diet is so essential during this time and covered key food groups to assist you to make healthier food choices.

Next, we will take a look at some important lifestyle tips which can help.

Lifestyle tips

The good news is there are a number of changes you can make to your day-to-day routine to help you feel more in control.

We've talked about the importance of diet to help nourish your body during this transition, however, there are also a range of lifestyle factors that can have an impact on how you experience symptoms of the menopause. In what follows we'll turn to look at some lifestyle tips that can help you to navigate a smoother transition through the menopause.

Hydration

Keeping hydrated is important for all human beings at any stage of life. Ensuring an adequate fluid intake allows the body to remove toxins and waste products from the body and make sure all our cells are functioning correctly. The body is 60% water, so it's no wonder water intake plays such a key role in our overall health. The general recommendation for adults is to consume 2 litres of non-caffeinated, sugar-free liquid every day.

When it comes to menopause, there is evidence to suggest that dehydration impacts thermoregulatory control with low water intake being linked to increased body temperatures [48]. Therefore, maintaining good fluid intake may assist in keeping body temperature under control as well as reducing the incidence of hot flushes. For those who experience night sweats, replenishing the lost fluid during the day is important to ensure you keep hydrated. If night sweats are problematic and frequent, you may want to consider topping up your drinks during the day with electrolytes, which are essential trace minerals such as sodium and potassium, to replace those that are lost in sweat. This can help to prevent muscle cramps and fatigue associated with low electrolyte levels.

Finally, as we have already discussed, skin health changes are very common and you may notice your skin becoming dry, irritated or thinner due to the decline in collagen production. Ensuring good hydration levels is essential to skin health and appearance as hydrated skin cells ensure optimal health and function as well as aiding with a more 'moisturised' appearance. Good hydration alongside an adequate intake of omega fatty acids is key to good skin health during this time.

Sleep

We all know the havoc that lack of sleep can play on our body. With insufficient sleep, we struggle with cognitive tasks and energy levels throughout the day. Therefore, obtaining the optimal amount of sleep is essential for both mental and physical performance. Experts recommend aiming for between seven and eight hours of quality sleep per night. However, this can feel impossible at points during the menopause with sleep disturbance being caused by a range of symptoms including hot flushes, night sweats, insomnia, breathing issues (such as sleep apnea), and struggles with mood, stress and anxiety.

There are some dietary and lifestyle changes we can consider to aid with a good night's sleep. For example, avoiding caffeine, nicotine or alcohol - particularly in the late afternoon and evenings - has been shown to improve sleep patterns [49]. Maintaining a healthy weight (or weight loss in those who are overweight) has demonstrated a reduction in the severity of hot flushes [50]. For those who suffer night sweats, keeping the bedroom cool and well ventilated can help to reduce body temperature and therefore the potential occurrence for hot flushes and night sweats. Also, wearing light, cotton nightwear and using cotton bed sheets can help to keep our body temperatures lower than some synthetic materials.

Spicy food, caffeine, alcohol and smoking

We have covered the foundations of maintaining a healthy diet already, however there are certain habits and consumptions which can act as triggers for various menopausal symptoms. Hot, spicy foods can be a real issue for some as these raise the core body temperature and in turn increase the likelihood of a hot flush due to the reduced function of the hypothalamus.

A high intake of caffeine can also have a similar vasomotor effect thereby increasing the risk of hot flushes and night sweats [51]. Additionally, associations have also been made between a high caffeine intake and accelerated bone loss in postmenopausal women [52]. Reducing caffeine intake and replacing with sugar-free drinks such as water, flavoured water and herbal teas are a good way to ensure a sufficient fluid intake without relying on caffeinated beverages.

Interestingly, research has been conducted on the correlation between alcohol consumption and the age of the menopause onset. A study reviewing the research in this area and looking at a large pool of women noted a link between higher intakes of alcohol and an earlier onset of the menopause, however the potential mechanism of action for this is unknown and more research still needs to be done in this area [53].

Smoking is also associated with more severe symptoms of menopause. Data from a study looking into the link between menopausal symptoms and smoking found that the proportion of someone's lifetime spent smoking - rather than the number of cigarettes smoked per day - was significantly associated with more intense symptoms compared against those who smoked for a shorter length of time or didn't smoke at all [54].

Reducing toxic exposure

We come into contact with toxins in our everyday life from pollution in the air we breathe to chemicals in our household products. These toxins can also be found in food, drinking water and personal care products.

Xenoestrogens are found in everyday items but very commonly plastic containers which can get into our bodies through consumption or skin contact. As the name eludes, xenoestrogens have an 'oestrogen like effect' and can disrupt our normal hormone balance. They exert no beneficial effect and only exacerbate the symptoms of menopause. Additionally, they are not easy to break down by the body therefore they are readily stored in our fat cells long term. This can lead to a harmful build up increasing the risk of certain hormone associated cancers [55].

Opting for filtered water can help avoid common toxins found in drinking water and choosing organic produce where possible can also mean you avoid chemicals and pesticides commonly used while farming. Choose eco-friendly, chemical free household and personal care products to reduce contact with toxins through your skin.

Physical activity

As with all stages of life, physical activity is well known to have a large beneficial effect on our health, from improved markers of cardiovascular health through to enhanced cognition and mental health. Physical activity, and in particular 'weight-bearing' type exercises, are especially important during the menopause as this type of activity helps to improve bone density at a time where bone health is at risk. Weight-bearing exercises put a safe amount of stress on the bones which in turn signals for the body to strengthen and increase the bone matrix density. Weight-bearing activity can include walking, jogging, aerobics, dancing, pilates, jumping or any other action which involves holding up your body weight. Strength or resistance training can also be beneficial as this helps to strengthen the tissues and muscles surrounding the bones which reduces the risk of falls and damage [56].

As well as benefitting bone health, increased physical activity also improves cardiovascular health markers even more so than weight loss can [57], therefore helping to minimise the risks that lowered oestrogen can have on the cardiovascular and metabolic systems.

See page 32, 'Strength Exercises' written by fitness coach, Dawn French, designed during her own menopausal experience to help offset symptoms, build bone and muscle strength and reduce weight gain.

Cognition and mental health can also greatly benefit from regular exercise. Anxiety is a common symptom of the menopause, however, there is ample evidence to suggest that partaking in low to moderate intensity exercise on a weekly basis can help improve this in middle-aged and older women [58]. This outcome has also been observed for those going through menopause with depressive symptoms. It was found that those with depression had more menopausal symptoms and experienced them more severely than those who were not depressed. Similarly, the same study found that those who exercised regularly were less likely to be depressed and were less symptomatic than those who did not exercise often [59].

Frequent exercise plays an important role in maintaining a healthy weight which can be more difficult at this time. Although 'weight gain' alone cannot be attributed to the menopause [60, 61] the re-distribution of fat in the abdominal area can put individuals at increased risk of factors associated with being overweight. This is because abdominal or visceral fat is stored around the body's organs and this type of fat in particular is linked to an increased risk of cardiovascular disease and metabolic syndrome compared to fat that sits underneath the skin surface. The good news is that both dietary and lifestyle improvements including exercise can prevent weight gain and lessen waist circumference in peri and postmenopausal women [62].

Mood and mind

Mood and mind in menopausal women can be greatly affected and this may lead to a variety of symptoms including anxiety, depression, brain fog or cognitive impairment. As previously mentioned, exercise can be a great way to help reduce some of the feelings of low mood experienced in menopausal women.

As well as improving physical activity levels, cognitive behavioural therapy (CBT) can assist with several issues relating to mental health. This non-medical approach is a talking therapy that can provide practical coping mechanisms and skills to manage specific problems, both physical and psychological. A recent study has demonstrated how CBT can help cope with managing menopausal hot flushes in public [63]. CBT can be accessed online via NHS and surgery websites, through your GP or you can sign up to private clinics that offer this service.

Meditation can be another useful way to clear your mind from daily stressors and assist with positive feelings of well-being. Research indicates that mind-body training techniques like meditation, yoga, and tai chi are safe and effective methods that can easily be practiced in a wide variety of situations. Such mindfulness exercises have been shown to assist with improving mental health, reducing musculoskeletal pain, and lessening menopausal symptoms including sleep disturbances and hot flushes [64]

Food supplements

As well as ensuring a wholesome and well-balanced diet, food supplements can play a key role in overall health and assist with some of the common symptoms of menopause.

The sad truth is that even with a well-balanced, nutritious and wholefood diet, the soil isn't what it used to be, and essential nutrients have leached from the soil over the years due to over farming and the use of artificial fertilisers and chemicals. This means that we are not getting the same level of nutrients from our foods as we were 70 years ago [65]. This is another reason to support and opt for organic produce which doesn't rely so heavily on intensive farming practices and avoids the use of chemicals which is detrimental to the soil enrichment and the surrounding environment.

Using food supplements correctly can work as a practical tool to ensure our bodies are receiving the optimal level of essential nutrients when gaps may become evident. This can be due to a variety of factors including allergies, dietary choices, intolerances and food availability.

It is important to note, however, that not all food supplements are made the same. When deciding on a food supplement that's right for you, it is always best to seek guidance from a qualified nutritionist or your local independent health food store.

My top tips when choosing a food supplement:

- Look for products which only contain 100% active ingredients and do not use any unnecessary binders, fillers, glues, sugars, artificial colours, preservatives or additives.

- Look for supplements packaged in glass amber jars to protect the contents from heat, light and moisture and avoid plastic pots as certain plastics are capable of leaching xenoestrogens and other chemicals such as PCBs and BPAs into their contents.

- Finally, it is good practice to dig a bit deeper and find out about the company who formulates and produces the food supplement. Where are they based? What standards and accreditations do they hold? Is a qualified team of nutritionists formulating the products for safe and therapeutic use? This will help give you reassurance that you are choosing a supplement that is right for you and which is credible and safe.

- See page 298 for a glossary of key supporting supplements.

Physical activity

Whether you're planning ahead and aiming to get your body 'menopause-fit', or you're already experiencing symptoms, adding strength training into your daily routine is a must.

Strength training won't turn you into a bodybuilder, but it will increase your muscle strength to help now and in later life. It will enhance your bone density (reduced risk of osteoporosis and fractures) and help lift your mood. The toughest part of exercise is just getting off the sofa and putting on your trainers, but once you get started, and begin tracking your progress in this journal, your body will thank you forever.

For this section of the journal, I've worked with Dawn French who is a qualified Fitness Coach. She has experienced the menopause and created a series of exercises which she uses herself as well as recommending to clients. For more information, please visit www.twdfitness.co.uk

Strength training

As we age, our muscles and bones become weaker, our flexibility decreases, posture and balance are less stable. Many women also notice weight gain during this time in their lives.

Strength training becomes more important than ever for women going through the peri/menopause because it slows down physical aging by increasing muscle mass and improving bone density. It helps prevent osteoporosis and boosts your metabolism, helping to reduce body fat.

I believe strength training is one the best forms of exercise for women at this stage in their lives, combined with exercise such as pilates, yoga, swimming or brisk walking.

Women often shy away from lifting weights for fear of getting too bulky but it takes years of disciplined weight training for this to happen so you don't need to worry. Lifting weights has so many benefits which is why I recommend to get started now if you are not doing this already.

We can gain so many benefits from strength training if we incorporate it into our weekly routine. Aim to include strength training at least two days per week with a home workout, a group class or a gym session. Try not to think of it as another chore to fit into your day but rather a positive time to spend building a stronger body and mind. Teaming up with a friend can help you keep motivated and encouraged too.

It is never too late to start and experience the wonderful benefits of strength training, especially during this time of your life.

Starting out

To begin with, you can use your own body weight as a resistance and the aim is to start slowly. The aim is to feel challenged at the end of each set but not to the point that the exercise is not being performed correctly. As you become stronger, you can start to add some resistance in the form of bands, dumbbells and kettlebells. If you don't have any equipment yet, then no worries. Get a couple of cans in the kitchen or fill up some water bottles. Make sure they're heavy enough for you to lift. If water is not enough, put sand in it instead!

If you are used to exercising with weight, the main focus is to ensure you are using a weight that feels challenging enough for each exercise. If you have been feeling comfortable in your workouts and haven't changed your weights in a while, now is the time to do so to ensure you continue to build muscle. Choose a weight that tires the muscles by the last two reps while still maintaining good form. You can also try adding another set. Changing the tempo of the movement is another great way to challenge your workout. For example, lowering for a count of three and lifting for one.

I love to combine lifting weight with bodyweight exercises and included in the following pages is a circuit style workout I recommend which can be adapted for any level, from complete beginner to those who have been used to exercising for some time. This can be done at home or at the gym where more equipment is available.

Find some time, on 2-3 days per week, to complete the 7 exercises on the following pages. Repeat each exercise 8-12 times, taking rest in between as needed. Then start again at the beginning of the set and repeat 2-4 times. Although completing 2-4 sets of the exercises, 2-3 times per week is ideal, don't be too hard on yourself if you can't always fit this in, doing whatever you can is a great start, and it all helps.

Good luck and feel free to follow me on Instagram @transformwithdawnfitness for more support.

Dawn French

Fitness Coach

1
Squat

2
Shoulder press

3
Lunge

Bent over row

Glute raise

Press up

Sit up

Planning your goals

It is worth taking some time before starting the journal to think about where you would like to be in 3-4 months' time. Quite often, other pressures on your time, such as work and family mean you put your own needs last. Creating a plan will give you clarity on what is important in your life, how you want to be feeling and allow you to focus on yourself.

Now you've read about the impact of nutrition, diet and lifestyle, you are armed with knowledge to help you control this next phase of your life and choose your own path through the menopause and beyond.

When setting goals, it's important to think of them in a positive way and understand what the goals will actually mean if you achieve them. How can you make them tangible and how will you know when you have achieved them. The answers you fill in below don't have to be big and audacious, sometimes the smallest things make the most difference. Be mindful of what is realistic, you can always set yourself new goals once you've achieved these ones.

How I feel now:

Things that make me smile:

Things I am grateful for:

My greatest strengths:

What I want to
improve:

_____

_____

_____

_____

_____

_____

Things I want to
do more of:

_____

_____

_____

_____

_____

_____

Ways to be kind
to myself:

_____

_____

_____

_____

_____

_____

How will I know when
I have improved?

_____

_____

_____

_____

_____

How will I make the
time to do them?

_____

_____

_____

_____

_____

How will I achieve
these?

_____

_____

_____

_____

_____

Other goals I'd like to achieve:

_____

_____

_____

People that can help and support me through my journey:

_____

_____

_____

Track and target your symptoms

Over the next few pages, you'll find space to record your symptoms and experience of the menopause. Fill this out over 2-4 weeks (it is recommended to complete a month so you can record your experiences and habits through a full cycle).

Once complete, the information can be shared with a health practitioner to allow them to help formulate the most suitable medication, supplements and lifestyle advice for you. This might mean starting a discussion with your GP who can give you an overview of the medical interventions available as a starting point.

In addition to this, independent health stores are a great source of advice where you will find experienced practitioners trained in nutrition and lifestyle advice. The experts here can support with a holistic approach to help you maintain long term health and wellbeing. You can find your nearest at www.findahealthstore.com. After the 'Track' pages, there is a space to record their recommendations, which will allow you to note down the different options and reflect on what your next steps might be.

Tips to complete the 'Track' pages:

Symptoms

Use the list on the right as a guide to add in the symptoms you are experiencing and score their impact. The list of symptoms provided is not exhaustive and you may find you have others in addition. If this is the case, note those down as well. There are no right or wrong symptoms, but it is important that every aspect is recorded so you can get the most appropriate treatment plan. Please be aware that some symptoms may have other causes so it is important to get advice from a healthcare professional.

Diet

Use this section to record what you eat throughout the day. This will help both you and your health practitioner understand your eating habits and patterns, as well as helping to identify possible links between diet and symptoms. Make sure you include your main meals along with any drinks and snacks too.

Activity

Write down the different types of activity you do along with the duration of each. Make sure you include exercise, but also don't forget to write down things like walking to work, gardening and housework. It all counts!

Mood

Quite often physical and emotional symptoms are linked so making a note of how you feel overall can guide a health practitioner in how best to support you.

Sleep

Aiming for between 7 and 8 hours of quality sleep a night is recommended. Less sleep or broken/poor quality sleep can lead to symptoms getting worse so noting down how you feel when you wake up and the number of hours you slept for will help identify if any changes in this area could help you.

Potential symptoms

Brain fog (memory)	Joint pain
Difficulty concentrating	Aching muscles
Hot flushes	Breast tenderness
Night sweats	Dry skin
Anxiety	Thinning skin
Panic attack	Itchiness
Anger	Thinning hair
Insomnia	Weaker bones
Low mood	Brittle nails
Mood swings	Gum problems
Low energy	Irregular menstrual cycle
Fatigue	Heavier periods
Irritability	Bodyfat increase
Stress	Headaches/migraines
Vaginal dryness	Dizziness
Loss of libido	Nausea
Painful intercourse	Bloating
Urinary tract infections	Irritable bowel
Weak bladder	Development of allergies
High cholesterol	Body odour changes
Heart palpitations	Tinnitus

 **Track Your Symptoms**

Gather 2-4 weeks of data to share with your health practitioner and/or an advisor in your local independent health food store. This information will help devise your personalised menopause support programme. Start any day of the week.

	Symptoms Fill in the symptoms you are experiencing. Reference the list on page 39. Score symptoms from 0 (very low) to 5 (extreme).	**Activity** E.g. walking, weight bearing exercise, classes
Day 1 Date		
Day 2 Date		
Day 3 Date		
Day 4 Date		

Tracking Start Date : ....

Date of Last Period : ....

Current Weight : ....

Week One

Diet — What are you eating each day?	Mood — How do you feel overall?	Sleep — Quality and hours?	Water — How many litres?
	Great Good Up & Down Low	Great Okay Poor Hours:	
	Great Good Up & Down Low	Great Okay Poor Hours:	
	Great Good Up & Down Low	Great Okay Poor Hours:	
	Great Good Up & Down Low	Great Okay Poor Hours:	

Track Your Symptoms

	Symptoms Fill in the symptoms you are experiencing. Reference the list on page 39. Score symptoms from 0 (very low) to 5 (extreme).	**Activity** E.g walking, weight bearing exercise, classes
Day 5 Date		
Day 6 Date		
Day 7 Date:		

Notes to share with your Healthcare Advisor

Prescription Medications:

Diet What are you eating each day?	Mood How do you feel overall?	Sleep Quality and hours?	Water How many litres?
	Great Good Up & Down Low	Great Okay Poor Hours:	
	Great Good Up & Down Low	Great Okay Poor Hours:	
	Great Good Up & Down Low	Great Okay Poor Hours:	

Supplements:

Allergies:

Track Your Symptoms

	Symptoms Fill in the symptoms you are experiencing. Reference the list on page 39. Score symptoms from 0 (very low) to 5 (extreme).	**Activity** E.g. walking, weight bearing exercise, classes
Day 8 Date		
Day 9 Date		
Day 10 Date		
Day 11 Date		

Week Two

Diet What are you eating each day?	Mood How do you feel overall?	Sleep Quality and hours?	Water How many litres?
	Great Good Up & Down Low	Great Okay Poor Hours:	
	Great Good Up & Down Low	Great Okay Poor Hours:	
	Great Good Up & Down Low	Great Okay Poor Hours:	
	Great Good Up & Down Low	Great Okay Poor Hours:	

Track Your Symptoms

	Symptoms Fill in the symptoms you are experiencing. Reference the list on page 39. Score symptoms from 0 (very low) to 5 (extreme).	**Activity** E.g walking, weight bearing exercise, classes
Day 12 Date		
Day 13 Date		
Day 14 Date:		

Notes to share with your Healthcare Advisor

Prescription Medications:

Diet What are you eating each day?	**Mood** How do you feel overall?	**Sleep** Quality and hours?	**Water** How many litres?
	Great ___ Good ___ Up & Down ___ Low	Great ___ Okay ___ Poor ___ Hours:	
	Great ___ Good ___ Up & Down ___ Low	Great ___ Okay ___ Poor ___ Hours:	
	Great ___ Good ___ Up & Down ___ Low	Great ___ Okay ___ Poor ___ Hours:	

Supplements:

Allergies:

Track Your
Symptoms

	Symptoms Fill in the symptoms you are experiencing. Reference the list on page 39. Score symptoms from 0 (very low) to 5 (extreme).	**Activity** E.g. walking, weight bearing exercise, classes
Day 15 Date		
Day 16 Date		
Day 17 Date		
Day 18 Date		

Week Three

Diet	Mood	Sleep	Water
What are you eating each day?	How do you feel overall?	Quality and hours?	How many litres?
	Great ——— Good ——— Up & Down ——— Low	Great ——— Okay ——— Poor ——— Hours:	
	Great ——— Good ——— Up & Down ——— Low	Great ——— Okay ——— Poor ——— Hours:	
	Great ——— Good ——— Up & Down ——— Low	Great ——— Okay ——— Poor ——— Hours:	
	Great ——— Good ——— Up & Down ——— Low	Great ——— Okay ——— Poor ——— Hours:	

Track Your Symptoms

	Symptoms Fill in the symptoms you are experiencing. Reference the list on page 39. Score symptoms from 0 (very low) to 5 (extreme).	**Activity** E.g walking, weight bearing exercise, classes
Day 19 Date		
Day 20 Date		
Day 21 Date:		

Notes to share with your Healthcare Advisor

Prescription Medications:

Diet What are you eating each day?	Mood How do you feel overall?	Sleep Quality and hours?	Water How many litres?
	Great ——— Good ——— Up & Down ——— Low	Great ——— Okay ——— Poor ——— Hours:	
	Great ——— Good ——— Up & Down ——— Low	Great ——— Okay ——— Poor ——— Hours:	
	Great ——— Good ——— Up & Down ——— Low	Great ——— Okay ——— Poor ——— Hours:	

Supplements:

Allergies:

Track Your Symptoms

	Symptoms Fill in the symptoms you are experiencing. Reference the list on page 39. Score symptoms from 0 (very low) to 5 (extreme).	**Activity** E.g. walking, weight bearing exercise, classes
Day 22 Date		
Day 23 Date		
Day 24 Date		
Day 25 Date		

Week Four

Diet What are you eating each day?	Mood How do you feel overall?	Sleep Quality and hours?	Water How many litres?
	Great Good Up & Down Low	Great Okay Poor Hours:	
	Great Good Up & Down Low	Great Okay Poor Hours:	
	Great Good Up & Down Low	Great Okay Poor Hours:	
	Great Good Up & Down Low	Great Okay Poor Hours:	

Track Your Symptoms

	Symptoms Fill in the symptoms you are experiencing. Reference the list on page 39. Score symptoms from 0 (very low) to 5 (extreme).	**Activity** E.g walking, weight bearing exercise, classes
Day 26 Date		
Day 27 Date		
Day 28 Date:		

Notes to share with your Healthcare Advisor

Prescription Medications:

Almost There!

Diet What are you eating each day?	Mood How do you feel overall?	Sleep Quality and hours?	Water How many litres?
	Great Good Up & Down Low	Great Okay Poor Hours:	
	Great Good Up & Down Low	Great Okay Poor Hours:	
	Great Good Up & Down Low	Great Okay Poor Hours:	

Supplements:

Allergies:

Target Your Symptoms

Record your personalised plan of action devised with help from your health practitioner and/or an advisor in your local independent health food store.

Discover a Local Independent Advisor:

FindAHealthStore.com

Menopause specific supplements

Symptoms:

_____

_____

_____

_____

_____

_____

Supporting supplements:

_____

_____

_____

_____

_____

_____

Foundation supplements

Multivitamin:

_____

_____

Probiotic:

_____

_____

Omega oil:

_____

_____

Medication: _____

_____

_____

Name of your healthcare advisor:

Date of review:

....

....

Diet

Foods to include:

_____

_____

_____

_____

_____

_____

Recommended
water intake: _____

Foods to avoid:

_____

_____

_____

_____

_____

_____

Activity - Best types of activity, suggestions of local classes, recommended professionals:

_____

_____

_____

Lifestyle tips - Day to day advice, details of support groups:

_____

_____

_____

_____

Notes

Thrive through your menopause

Here is where you start to see the positive impact of your treatment plan and measure the progress you are making.

This section covers 90 days, which is the recommended time to allow changes in diet and lifestyle to take effect. The pages are split into seven-day sections so you can see week-by-week how things are improving for you.

Each page is a space for you to record your day, how you are feeling and sleeping, a place to keep track of the supplements you are taking, as well as your diet and a measure of the symptoms you are experiencing. Use it in the way that works best for you – add doodles, colour coding, your favourite quotes – it's your space to record your menopause experience.

Symptoms

Record your symptoms and how much they impact you. Adding a total score should enable you to flick back through completed pages to give a quick indication of progress. The lower the score, the better you should feel. Please do bear in mind that it takes time for your body to respond and adjust to lifestyle interventions, so it may take a few weeks to see any changes. Don't be disheartened if your progress isn't linear – it's perfectly normal for symptoms and feelings to fluctuate, but what is important is the overall picture of progress.

Diet

Note down what you are eating each day. Aim for a balanced diet as described earlier in the journal. By noting everything you eat, you'll be able to see if any particular foods are linked to symptoms. Please see page 16 for more information.

Activity

Aim for at least 2.5 hours of exercise per week with moderate intensity to increase your breathing and heart rate. Remember that during perimenopause and menopause, it is important to incorporate some weight bearing activity. This type of exercise works directly on the bones in your legs, hips and lower spine to slow mineral loss. Examples include jogging, rope skipping, step aerobics, heavy gardening, badminton, hiking, dancing and climbing stairs. Make it fun with group exercise classes, get competitive with a family tennis match, or incorporate exercise into your daily routine (e.g. cycle to work) to help you reach and exceed the weekly target!

As you reach the end of each week, take the chance to review where you are at and if you need more advice from your health practitioner. There is also an exercise to complete and spaces to make your own notes and thoughts. This is your journal so feel free to use it in the way that works for you. There really is no right or wrong, it's here to help you find the path that works for you and give you the tools to have your menopause, your way.

Day 1

Complete daily for 90 days as you implement and adjust your personalised menopause support programme and measure your progress. After one month, pop back into your local independent health food store to discuss your progress. After 90 days, if you'd like to help others, share your story on social media #themenopausejournal

Date: ....

Reference the List on Page 39

Symptoms - Fill in the symptoms you are experiencing.

Symptoms:	Comments	Score
_____	_____	____
_____	_____	____
_____	_____	____
_____	_____	____
_____	_____	____
_____	_____	____
_____	_____	____

Score symptoms from 0 (very low) to 5 (extreme)   **Total Score** _____

Activity - E.g. walking, weight exercise, classes   **Duration**

Type:
_____   ____
_____   ____
_____   ____

| How do you feel overall? | Great | Good | Up & Down | Low | How did you sleep? | Great | Good | Poor | Hrs: ___ |

Diet - What did you eat today?

Did you have any of these phytoestrogenic foods today?

O Soy beans – edamame, tofu

O Peas and beans

O Lentils

O Seeds – flaxseed, sesame

O Fruits – banana, apple, orange

O Wholegrain and wheat bran

O Vegetables – cauliflower, broccoli, carrots, cabbage

O Berries and currants

O Other

See Page 17 for More Details

Total water intake (aim for 8 large glasses):

O   O   O   O   O   O   O   O

If you could summarise today in 3 words, what would they be?

1.   **2.**   **3.**

Thrive
Day 2

Date: ....

Reference the List on Page 39

Symptoms - Fill in the symptoms you are experiencing.		
Symptoms:	Comments	Score
_____	_____	_____
_____	_____	_____
_____	_____	_____
_____	_____	_____
_____	_____	_____
_____	_____	_____
_____	_____	_____
_____	_____	_____

Score symptoms from 0 (very low) to 5 (extreme)   **Total Score** _____

Activity - E.g. walking, weight exercise, classes	**Duration**
Type:	
_____	_____
_____	_____
_____	_____

How do you feel overall?   Great | Good | Up & Down | Low

How did you sleep?   Great | Good | Poor | Hrs: ___

Diet - What did you eat today?

Did you have any of these phytoestrogenic foods today?

O Soy beans – edamame, tofu

O Peas and beans

O Lentils

O Seeds – flaxseed, sesame

O Fruits – banana, apple, orange

O Wholegrain and wheat bran

O Vegetables – cauliflower, broccoli, carrots, cabbage

O Berries and currants

O Other

Total water intake (aim for 8 large glasses):

O   O   O   O   O   O   O   O

See Page 17 for More Details

If you could summarise today in 3 words, what would they be?

1.

2.

3.

Thrive
Day 3

Date: ....

Reference the List on Page 39

Symptoms - Fill in the symptoms you are experiencing.

Symptoms:	Comments	Score
_____	_____	____
_____	_____	____
_____	_____	____
_____	_____	____
_____	_____	____
_____	_____	____
_____	_____	____

Score symptoms from 0 (very low) to 5 (extreme)   **Total Score** _____

Activity - E.g. walking, weight exercise, classes   **Duration**

Type:

_____   _____

_____   _____

_____   _____

| How do you feel overall? | Great \| Good \| Up & Down \| Low | How did you sleep? | Great \| Good \| Poor \| Hrs: ___ |

Diet - What did you eat today?

Did you have any of these phytoestrogenic foods today?

O Soy beans – edamame, tofu

O Peas and beans

O Lentils

O Seeds – flaxseed, sesame

O Fruits – banana, apple, orange

O Wholegrain and wheat bran

O Vegetables – cauliflower, broccoli, carrots, cabbage

O Berries and currants

O Other

See Page 17 for More Details

Total water intake (aim for 8 large glasses):

O   O   O   O   O   O   O   O

If you could summarise today in 3 words, what would they be?

1.

2.

3.

Thrive
Day 4

Date: ....

Reference the List on Page 39

Symptoms - Fill in the symptoms you are experiencing.

Symptoms:	Comments	Score
_____	_____	_____
_____	_____	_____
_____	_____	_____
_____	_____	_____
_____	_____	_____
_____	_____	_____
_____	_____	_____
_____	_____	_____

Score symptoms from 0 (very low) to 5 (extreme)   **Total Score** _____

Activity - E.g. walking, weight exercise, classes   **Duration**

Type:

_____   _____

_____   _____

_____   _____

| How do you feel overall? | Great \| Good \| Up & Down \| Low | How did you sleep? | Great \| Good \| Poor \| Hrs: ___ |

Diet - What did you eat today?

Did you have any of these phytoestrogenic foods today?

O Soy beans – edamame, tofu

O Peas and beans

O Lentils

O Seeds – flaxseed, sesame

O Fruits – banana, apple, orange

O Wholegrain and wheat bran

O Vegetables – cauliflower, broccoli, carrots, cabbage

O Berries and currants

O Other

See Page 17 for More Details

Total water intake (aim for 8 large glasses):

O   O   O   O   O   O   O   O

If you could summarise today in 3 words, what would they be?

1.

2.

3.

Thrive
Day 5

Date: ....

Reference the List on Page 39

Symptoms - Fill in the symptoms you are experiencing.

Symptoms:	Comments	Score
_____	_____	_____
_____	_____	_____
_____	_____	_____
_____	_____	_____
_____	_____	_____
_____	_____	_____
_____	_____	_____

Score symptoms from 0 (very low) to 5 (extreme)   **Total Score** _____

Activity - E.g. walking, weight exercise, classes   **Duration**

Type:

_____   _____

_____   _____

_____   _____

| How do you feel overall? | Great │ Good │ Up & Down │ Low | How did you sleep? | Great │ Good │ Poor │ Hrs: ____ |

Diet - What did you eat today?

Did you have any of these phytoestrogenic foods today?

O Soy beans – edamame, tofu

O Peas and beans

O Lentils

O Seeds – flaxseed, sesame

O Fruits – banana, apple, orange

O Wholegrain and wheat bran

O Vegetables – cauliflower, broccoli, carrots, cabbage

O Berries and currants

O Other

See Page 17 for More Details

Total water intake (aim for 8 large glasses):

O   O   O   O   O   O   O   O

If you could summarise today in 3 words, what would they be?

1.

2.

3.

Thrive
Day 6

Date: ....

Reference the List on Page 39

Symptoms - Fill in the symptoms you are experiencing.

Symptoms:	Comments	Score
_____	_____	_____
_____	_____	_____
_____	_____	_____
_____	_____	_____
_____	_____	_____
_____	_____	_____
_____	_____	_____
_____	_____	_____

Score symptoms from 0 (very low) to 5 (extreme)   **Total Score** _____

Activity - E.g. walking, weight exercise, classes   **Duration**

Type:

_____   _____

_____   _____

_____

| How do you feel overall? | Great | Good | Up & Down | Low | How did you sleep? | Great | Good | Poor | Hrs: ____ |

Diet - What did you eat today?

Did you have any of these phytoestrogenic foods today?

O Soy beans – edamame, tofu

O Peas and beans

O Lentils

O Seeds – flaxseed, sesame

O Fruits – banana, apple, orange

O Wholegrain and wheat bran

O Vegetables – cauliflower, broccoli, carrots, cabbage

O Berries and currants

O Other

Total water intake (aim for 8 large glasses):

O   O   O   O   O   O   O   O

See Page 17 for More Details

If you could summarise today in 3 words, what would they be?

1.

2.

3.

Day 7

Date: ....

Reference the List on Page 39

Symptoms - Fill in the symptoms you are experiencing.

Symptoms:	Comments	Score
_____	_____	_____
_____	_____	_____
_____	_____	_____
_____	_____	_____
_____	_____	_____
_____	_____	_____
_____	_____	_____
_____	_____	_____

Score symptoms from 0 (very low) to 5 (extreme)   **Total Score** _____

Activity - E.g. walking, weight exercise, classes   **Duration**

Type:
_____ _____
_____ _____
_____ _____

| How do you feel overall? | Great \| Good \| Up & Down \| Low | How did you sleep? | Great \| Good \| Poor \| Hrs: ___ |

Diet - What did you eat today?

Did you have any of these phytoestrogenic foods today?

O Soy beans – edamame, tofu

O Peas and beans

O Lentils

O Seeds – flaxseed, sesame

O Fruits – banana, apple, orange

O Wholegrain and wheat bran

O Vegetables – cauliflower, broccoli, carrots, cabbage

O Berries and currants

O Other

See Page 17 for More Details

Total water intake (aim for 8 large glasses):

O   O   O   O   O   O   O   O

If you could summarise today in 3 words, what would they be?

1.

2.

3.

Maya Angelou

" I'm grateful to be a woman. I must have done something great in another life. "

The *Nature* Exercise

Connecting with the Earth and her natural rhythms enhances feelings of tranquillity for most people. Get comfortable, close your eyes and imagine your favourite natural place. It could be a beach, in a forest, climbing a mountain or at a local park. Relax and enjoy this space for a few minutes. Imagine the colours, the temperature, the feel of the grass or sand under your bare feet, enjoy the sensations.

Open your eyes and write down everything you remember and re-read your description whenever you feel you need a 'happy place'.

This exercise can be repeated as often as is needed.

Thrive
Day 8

Date: ....

Reference the List on Page 39

Symptoms - Fill in the symptoms you are experiencing.

Symptoms:	Comments	Score
_____	_____	____
_____	_____	____
_____	_____	____
_____	_____	____
_____	_____	____
_____	_____	____
_____	_____	____

Score symptoms from 0 (very low) to 5 (extreme)　　　**Total Score** _____

Activity - E.g. walking, weight exercise, classes　　　**Duration**

Type:

_____　____

_____　____

_____　____

How do you feel overall? Great | Good | Up & Down | Low

How did you sleep? Great | Good | Poor | Hrs: ____

Diet - What did you eat today?

Did you have any of these phytoestrogenic foods today?

O Soy beans – edamame, tofu

O Peas and beans

O Lentils

O Seeds – flaxseed, sesame

O Fruits – banana, apple, orange

O Wholegrain and wheat bran

O Vegetables – cauliflower, broccoli, carrots, cabbage

O Berries and currants

O Other

Total water intake (aim for 8 large glasses):

O   O   O   O   O   O   O   O

See Page 17 for More Details

If you could summarise today in 3 words, what would they be?

1.

2.

3.

Thrive
Day 9

Date: ....

Reference the List on Page 39

Symptoms - Fill in the symptoms you are experiencing.

Symptoms:	Comments	Score
_____	_____	____
_____	_____	____
_____	_____	____
_____	_____	____
_____	_____	____
_____	_____	____
_____	_____	____

Score symptoms from 0 (very low) to 5 (extreme)   **Total Score** _____

Activity - E.g. walking, weight exercise, classes   **Duration**

Type:

_____   _____

_____   _____

_____   _____

How do you feel overall?   Great | Good | Up & Down | Low

How did you sleep?   Great | Good | Poor | Hrs: ___

Diet - What did you eat today?

Did you have any of these phytoestrogenic foods today?

O Soy beans – edamame, tofu

O Peas and beans

O Lentils

O Seeds – flaxseed, sesame

O Fruits – banana, apple, orange

O Wholegrain and wheat bran

O Vegetables – cauliflower, broccoli, carrots, cabbage

O Berries and currants

O Other

Total water intake (aim for 8 large glasses):

O   O   O   O   O   O   O   O

See Page 17 for More Details

If you could summarise today in 3 words, what would they be?

1.

2.

3.

Day 10

Date: ....

Reference the List on Page 39

Symptoms - Fill in the symptoms you are experiencing.		
Symptoms:	Comments	Score
_____	_____	____
_____	_____	____
_____	_____	____
_____	_____	____
_____	_____	____
_____	_____	____
_____	_____	____

Score symptoms from 0 (very low) to 5 (extreme)　　**Total Score** ____

Activity - E.g. walking, weight exercise, classes	**Duration**
Type:	
_____	____
_____	____
_____	____

How do you feel overall? Great | Good | Up & Down | Low

How did you sleep? Great | Good | Poor | Hrs: _____

Diet - What did you eat today?

Did you have any of these phytoestrogenic foods today?

O Soy beans – edamame, tofu

O Peas and beans

O Lentils

O Seeds – flaxseed, sesame

O Fruits – banana, apple, orange

O Wholegrain and wheat bran

O Vegetables – cauliflower, broccoli, carrots, cabbage

O Berries and currants

O Other

See Page 17 for More Details

Total water intake (aim for 8 large glasses):

O   O   O   O   O   O   O   O

If you could summarise today in 3 words, what would they be?

1.

2.

3.

Day 11

Date: ....

Reference the List on Page 39

Symptoms - Fill in the symptoms you are experiencing.

Symptoms:	Comments	Score
_____	_____	_____
_____	_____	_____
_____	_____	_____
_____	_____	_____
_____	_____	_____
_____	_____	_____
_____	_____	_____

Score symptoms from 0 (very low) to 5 (extreme)   **Total Score** _____

Activity - E.g. walking, weight exercise, classes   **Duration**

Type:

_____   _____

_____   _____

_____   _____

How do you feel overall?   Great | Good | Up & Down | Low

How did you sleep?   Great | Good | Poor | Hrs: ___

Diet - What did you eat today?

Did you have any of these phytoestrogenic foods today?

O Soy beans – edamame, tofu

O Peas and beans

O Lentils

O Seeds – flaxseed, sesame

O Fruits – banana, apple, orange

O Wholegrain and wheat bran

O Vegetables – cauliflower, broccoli, carrots, cabbage

O Berries and currants

O Other

See Page 17 for More Details

Total water intake (aim for 8 large glasses):

O   O   O   O   O   O   O   O

If you could summarise today in 3 words, what would they be?

1.

2.

3.

Day 12

Date: ....

Reference the List on Page 39

Symptoms - Fill in the symptoms you are experiencing.

Symptoms:	Comments	Score
_____	_____	____
_____	_____	____
_____	_____	____
_____	_____	____
_____	_____	____
_____	_____	____
_____	_____	____
_____	_____	____

Score symptoms from 0 (very low) to 5 (extreme)   **Total Score** ____

Activity - E.g. walking, weight exercise, classes   **Duration**

Type:

_____	____
_____	____
_____	____

How do you feel overall? Great | Good | Up & Down | Low

How did you sleep? Great | Good | Poor | Hrs: ____

Diet - What did you eat today?

Did you have any of these phytoestrogenic foods today?

O Soy beans – edamame, tofu

O Peas and beans

O Lentils

O Seeds – flaxseed, sesame

O Fruits – banana, apple, orange

O Wholegrain and wheat bran

O Vegetables – cauliflower, broccoli, carrots, cabbage

O Berries and currants

O Other

Total water intake (aim for 8 large glasses):

O   O   O   O   O   O   O   O

See Page 17 for More Details

If you could summarise today in 3 words, what would they be?

1.

2.

3.

Thrive
Day 13

Date: ....

⌐ Reference the List on Page 39

Symptoms - Fill in the symptoms you are experiencing.

Symptoms:	Comments	Score
_____	_____	_____
_____	_____	_____
_____	_____	_____
_____	_____	_____
_____	_____	_____
_____	_____	_____
_____	_____	_____

Score symptoms from 0 (very low) to 5 (extreme)   **Total Score** _____

Activity - E.g. walking, weight exercise, classes   **Duration**

Type:

_____   _____

_____   _____

_____   _____

How do you feel overall? Great | Good | Up & Down | Low

How did you sleep? Great | Good | Poor | Hrs: ___

Diet - What did you eat today?

Did you have any of these phytoestrogenic foods today?

O Soy beans – edamame, tofu

O Peas and beans

O Lentils

O Seeds – flaxseed, sesame

O Fruits – banana, apple, orange

O Wholegrain and wheat bran

O Vegetables – cauliflower, broccoli, carrots, cabbage

O Berries and currants

O Other

See Page 17 for More Details

Total water intake (aim for 8 large glasses):

O   O   O   O   O   O   O   O

If you could summarise today in 3 words, what would they be?

1.

2.

3.

Thrive
Day 14

Date: ....

Reference the List on Page 39

Symptoms - Fill in the symptoms you are experiencing.		
Symptoms:	Comments	Score
_____	_____	_____
_____	_____	_____
_____	_____	_____
_____	_____	_____
_____	_____	_____
_____	_____	_____
_____	_____	_____
_____	_____	_____

Score symptoms from 0 (very low) to 5 (extreme)   **Total Score** _____

Activity - E.g. walking, weight exercise, classes	**Duration**
Type:	
_____	_____
_____	_____
_____	_____

How do you feel overall?   Great | Good | Up & Down | Low

How did you sleep?   Great | Good | Poor | Hrs: ____

Diet - What did you eat today?

Did you have any of these phytoestrogenic foods today?

O Soy beans – edamame, tofu

O Peas and beans

O Lentils

O Seeds – flaxseed, sesame

O Fruits – banana, apple, orange

O Wholegrain and wheat bran

O Vegetables – cauliflower, broccoli, carrots, cabbage

O Berries and currants

O Other

See Page 17 for More Details

Total water intake (aim for 8 large glasses):

O   O   O   O   O   O   O   O

If you could summarise today in 3 words, what would they be?

1.

2.

3.

" It's not like 50 is the new 30. It's like 50 is the new chapter. "

Sharon Stone

The *Decision* Exercise

Are you struggling to make a decision?
Torn between two directions or options?
Write down a For & Against or Pros & Cons list.

Still undecided? Toss a coin and listen to
your gut reaction. You've got this!

For..

Against...

For..

Against...

For..

Against...

For..

Against...

For..

Against...

This exercise can be repeated as often as is needed.

Thrive
Day 15

Date: ....

Reference the List on Page 39

Symptoms - Fill in the symptoms you are experiencing.		
Symptoms:	Comments	Score
_____	_____	_____
_____	_____	_____
_____	_____	_____
_____	_____	_____
_____	_____	_____
_____	_____	_____
_____	_____	_____

Score symptoms from 0 (very low) to 5 (extreme) **Total Score** _____

Activity - E.g. walking, weight exercise, classes	**Duration**
Type:	
_____	_____
_____	_____
_____	_____

How do you feel overall? Great | Good | Up & Down | Low

How did you sleep? Great | Good | Poor | Hrs: ____

Diet - What did you eat today?

Did you have any of these phytoestrogenic foods today?

O Soy beans – edamame, tofu

O Peas and beans

O Lentils

O Seeds – flaxseed, sesame

O Fruits – banana, apple, orange

O Wholegrain and wheat bran

O Vegetables – cauliflower, broccoli, carrots, cabbage

O Berries and currants

O Other

See Page 17 for More Details

Total water intake (aim for 8 large glasses):

O   O   O   O   O   O   O   O

If you could summarise today in 3 words, what would they be?

1.

2.

3.

Thrive
Day 16

Date: ....

Reference the List on Page 39

Symptoms - Fill in the symptoms you are experiencing.

Symptoms:	Comments	Score
_____	_____	_____
_____	_____	_____
_____	_____	_____
_____	_____	_____
_____	_____	_____
_____	_____	_____
_____	_____	_____

Score symptoms from 0 (very low) to 5 (extreme)   **Total Score** _____

Activity - E.g. walking, weight exercise, classes   **Duration**

Type:

_____   _____

_____   _____

_____   _____

| How do you feel overall? | Great | Good | Up & Down | Low | How did you sleep? | Great | Good | Poor | Hrs: ____ |

Diet - What did you eat today?

Did you have any of these phytoestrogenic foods today?

O Soy beans – edamame, tofu

O Peas and beans

O Lentils

O Seeds – flaxseed, sesame

O Fruits – banana, apple, orange

O Wholegrain and wheat bran

O Vegetables – cauliflower, broccoli, carrots, cabbage

O Berries and currants

O Other

Total water intake (aim for 8 large glasses):

O   O   O   O   O   O   O   O

See Page 17 for More Details

If you could summarise today in 3 words, what would they be?

1.

2.

3.

Thrive
Day 17

Date: ....

Reference the List on Page 39

Symptoms - Fill in the symptoms you are experiencing.

Symptoms:	Comments	Score
_____	_____	_____
_____	_____	_____
_____	_____	_____
_____	_____	_____
_____	_____	_____
_____	_____	_____
_____	_____	_____

Score symptoms from 0 (very low) to 5 (extreme)   **Total Score** _____

Activity - E.g. walking, weight exercise, classes | Duration

Type:

_____ _____

_____ _____

_____ _____

| How do you feel overall? | Great | Good | Up & Down | Low | | How did you sleep? | Great | Good | Poor | Hrs: ___ |

Diet - What did you eat today?

Did you have any of these phytoestrogenic foods today?

O Soy beans – edamame, tofu

O Peas and beans

O Lentils

O Seeds – flaxseed, sesame

O Fruits – banana, apple, orange

O Wholegrain and wheat bran

O Vegetables – cauliflower, broccoli, carrots, cabbage

O Berries and currants

O Other

See Page 17 for More Details

Total water intake (aim for 8 large glasses):

O O O O O O O O

If you could summarise today in 3 words, what would they be?

1.   **2.**   **3.**

Thrive
Day 18

Date: ....

↙ Reference the List on Page 39

Symptoms - Fill in the symptoms you are experiencing.

Symptoms:	Comments	Score
_____	_____	_____
_____	_____	_____
_____	_____	_____
_____	_____	_____
_____	_____	_____
_____	_____	_____
_____	_____	_____

Score symptoms from 0 (very low) to 5 (extreme)   **Total Score** _____

Activity - E.g. walking, weight exercise, classes   **Duration**

Type:

_____   _____

_____   _____

_____

| How do you feel overall? | Great | Good | Up & Down | Low | How did you sleep? | Great | Good | Poor | Hrs: ___ |

Diet - What did you eat today?

Did you have any of these phytoestrogenic foods today?

O Soy beans – edamame, tofu

O Peas and beans

O Lentils

O Seeds – flaxseed, sesame

O Fruits – banana, apple, orange

O Wholegrain and wheat bran

O Vegetables – cauliflower, broccoli, carrots, cabbage

O Berries and currants

O Other

See Page 17 for More Details

Total water intake (aim for 8 large glasses):

O   O   O   O   O   O   O   O   O

If you could summarise today in 3 words, what would they be?

1.

2.

3.

Thrive
Day 19

Date: ....

Reference the List on Page 39

Symptoms - Fill in the symptoms you are experiencing.

Symptoms:	Comments	Score
_____	_____	_____
_____	_____	_____
_____	_____	_____
_____	_____	_____
_____	_____	_____
_____	_____	_____
_____	_____	_____

Score symptoms from 0 (very low) to 5 (extreme)   **Total Score** _____

Activity - E.g. walking, weight exercise, classes   **Duration**

Type:

_____   _____

_____   _____

_____   _____

How do you feel overall? Great | Good | Up & Down | Low

How did you sleep? Great | Good | Poor | Hrs: ____

Diet - What did you eat today?

Did you have any of these phytoestrogenic foods today?

O Soy beans – edamame, tofu

O Peas and beans

O Lentils

O Seeds – flaxseed, sesame

O Fruits – banana, apple, orange

O Wholegrain and wheat bran

O Vegetables – cauliflower, broccoli, carrots, cabbage

O Berries and currants

O Other

See Page 17 for More Details

Total water intake (aim for 8 large glasses):

O   O   O   O   O   O   O   O

If you could summarise today in 3 words, what would they be?

1.

2.

3.

Thrive
Day 20

Date: ....

Reference the List on Page 39

Symptoms - Fill in the symptoms you are experiencing.		
Symptoms:	**Comments**	**Score**
_____	_____	_____
_____	_____	_____
_____	_____	_____
_____	_____	_____
_____	_____	_____
_____	_____	_____
_____	_____	_____

Score symptoms from 0 (very low) to 5 (extreme)　　　**Total Score** _____

Activity - E.g. walking, weight exercise, classes	**Duration**
Type:	
_____	_____
_____	_____
_____	_____

| How do you feel overall? | Great | Good | Up & Down | Low | How did you sleep? | Great | Good | Poor | Hrs: _____ |

Diet - What did you eat today?

Did you have any of these phytoestrogenic foods today?

O Soy beans – edamame, tofu

O Peas and beans

O Lentils

O Seeds – flaxseed, sesame

O Fruits – banana, apple, orange

O Wholegrain and wheat bran

O Vegetables – cauliflower, broccoli, carrots, cabbage

O Berries and currants

O Other

See Page 17 for More Details

Total water intake (aim for 8 large glasses):

O   O   O   O   O   O   O   O

If you could summarise today in 3 words, what would they be?

1.

2.

3.

Day 21

Date: ....

Reference the List on Page 39

Symptoms - Fill in the symptoms you are experiencing.

Symptoms:	Comments	Score
_____	_____	____
_____	_____	____
_____	_____	____
_____	_____	____
_____	_____	____
_____	_____	____
_____	_____	____
_____	_____	____

Score symptoms from 0 (very low) to 5 (extreme)   **Total Score** _____

Activity - E.g. walking, weight exercise, classes   **Duration**

Type:

_____   _____

_____   _____

_____   _____

How do you feel overall?   Great | Good | Up & Down | Low

How did you sleep?   Great | Good | Poor | Hrs: ____

Diet - What did you eat today?

Did you have any of these phytoestrogenic foods today?

O Soy beans – edamame, tofu

O Peas and beans

O Lentils

O Seeds – flaxseed, sesame

O Fruits – banana, apple, orange

O Wholegrain and wheat bran

O Vegetables – cauliflower, broccoli, carrots, cabbage

O Berries and currants

O Other

See Page 17 for More Details

Total water intake (aim for 8 large glasses):

O   O   O   O   O   O   O   O

If you could summarise today in 3 words, what would they be?

1.

2.

3.

Kate Douglas Wiggin

" There is
a kind of
magicness
about going far away
and then coming back
all changed. "

The *Kindness* Exercise

Like most women, you are likely to be supportive in your family and community, but when was the last time you were kind to yourself?

Write down 5 things you are going to do this week to show yourself kindness. It could be something small like cooking yourself a special meal for one, or giving yourself a single hour to walk in nature alone, or go swimming.

1...

2...

3...

4...

5...

This exercise can be repeated as often as is needed.

Thrive
Day 22

Date: ....

Reference the List on Page 39

Symptoms - Fill in the symptoms you are experiencing.

Symptoms:	Comments	Score
_____	_____	_____
_____	_____	_____
_____	_____	_____
_____	_____	_____
_____	_____	_____
_____	_____	_____
_____	_____	_____

Score symptoms from 0 (very low) to 5 (extreme)   **Total Score** _____

Activity - E.g. walking, weight exercise, classes   **Duration**

Type:

_____   _____

_____   _____

_____   _____

| How do you feel overall? | Great | Good | Up & Down | Low | How did you sleep? | Great | Good | Poor | Hrs: ___ |

Diet - What did you eat today?

Did you have any of these phytoestrogenic foods today?

O Soy beans – edamame, tofu

O Peas and beans

O Lentils

O Seeds – flaxseed, sesame

O Fruits – banana, apple, orange

O Wholegrain and wheat bran

O Vegetables – cauliflower, broccoli, carrots, cabbage

O Berries and currants

O Other

Total water intake (aim for 8 large glasses):

O   O   O   O   O   O   O   O

See Page 17 for More Details

If you could summarise today in 3 words, what would they be?

1.

2.

3.

Thrive
Day 23

Date: ....

Reference the List on Page 39

Symptoms - Fill in the symptoms you are experiencing.

Symptoms:	Comments	Score
_____	_____	_____
_____	_____	_____
_____	_____	_____
_____	_____	_____
_____	_____	_____
_____	_____	_____
_____	_____	_____

Score symptoms from 0 (very low) to 5 (extreme)   **Total Score** _____

Activity - E.g. walking, weight exercise, classes   **Duration**

Type:

How do you feel overall? Great | Good | Up & Down | Low

How did you sleep? Great | Good | Poor | Hrs: ___

Diet - What did you eat today?

Did you have any of these phytoestrogenic foods today?

O Soy beans – edamame, tofu

O Peas and beans

O Lentils

O Seeds – flaxseed, sesame

O Fruits – banana, apple, orange

O Wholegrain and wheat bran

O Vegetables – cauliflower, broccoli, carrots, cabbage

O Berries and currants

O Other

See Page 17 for More Details

Total water intake (aim for 8 large glasses):

O   O   O   O   O   O   O   O

If you could summarise today in 3 words, what would they be?

1.

2.

3.

Day 24

Date: ....

Reference the List on Page 39

Symptoms - Fill in the symptoms you are experiencing.

Symptoms:	Comments	Score
_____	_____	_____
_____	_____	_____
_____	_____	_____
_____	_____	_____
_____	_____	_____
_____	_____	_____
_____	_____	_____
_____	_____	_____

Score symptoms from 0 (very low) to 5 (extreme) **Total Score** _____

Activity - E.g. walking, weight exercise, classes   Duration

Type:

_____ _____

_____ _____

_____ _____

| How do you feel overall? | Great | Good | Up & Down | Low | How did you sleep? | Great | Good | Poor | Hrs: ___ |

Diet - What did you eat today?

Did you have any of these phytoestrogenic foods today?

O Soy beans – edamame, tofu

O Peas and beans

O Lentils

O Seeds – flaxseed, sesame

O Fruits – banana, apple, orange

O Wholegrain and wheat bran

O Vegetables – cauliflower, broccoli, carrots, cabbage

O Berries and currants

O Other

See Page 17 for More Details

Total water intake (aim for 8 large glasses):

O   O   O   O   O   O   O   O

If you could summarise today in 3 words, what would they be?

1.

2.

3.

Thrive
Day 25

Date: ....

Reference the List on Page 39

Symptoms - Fill in the symptoms you are experiencing.

Symptoms:	Comments	Score
_____	_____	_____
_____	_____	_____
_____	_____	_____
_____	_____	_____
_____	_____	_____
_____	_____	_____
_____	_____	_____
_____	_____	_____

Score symptoms from 0 (very low) to 5 (extreme)   **Total Score** _____

Activity - E.g. walking, weight exercise, classes   Duration

Type:

_____ _____

_____ _____

| How do you feel overall? | Great | Good | Up & Down | Low | How did you sleep? | Great | Good | Poor | Hrs: ___ |

Diet - What did you eat today?

Did you have any of these phytoestrogenic foods today?

O Soy beans – edamame, tofu

O Peas and beans

O Lentils

O Seeds – flaxseed, sesame

O Fruits – banana, apple, orange

O Wholegrain and wheat bran

O Vegetables – cauliflower, broccoli, carrots, cabbage

O Berries and currants

O Other

See Page 17 for More Details

Total water intake (aim for 8 large glasses):

O   O   O   O   O   O   O   O

If you could summarise today in 3 words, what would they be?

1.

2.

3.

Thrive
Day 26

Date: ....

Reference the List on Page 39

Symptoms - Fill in the symptoms you are experiencing.

Symptoms:	Comments	Score
_____	_____	_____
_____	_____	_____
_____	_____	_____
_____	_____	_____
_____	_____	_____
_____	_____	_____
_____	_____	_____

Score symptoms from 0 (very low) to 5 (extreme)   **Total Score** _____

Activity - E.g. walking, weight exercise, classes   **Duration**

Type:

_____   _____

_____   _____

_____   _____

| How do you feel overall? | Great \| Good \| Up & Down \| Low | How did you sleep? | Great \| Good \| Poor \| Hrs: ___ |

Diet - What did you eat today?

Did you have any of these phytoestrogenic foods today?

O Soy beans – edamame, tofu

O Peas and beans

O Lentils

O Seeds – flaxseed, sesame

O Fruits – banana, apple, orange

O Wholegrain and wheat bran

O Vegetables – cauliflower, broccoli, carrots, cabbage

O Berries and currants

O Other

See Page 17 for More Details

Total water intake (aim for 8 large glasses):

O   O   O   O   O   O   O   O

If you could summarise today in 3 words, what would they be?

1.

2.

3.

Thrive
Day 27

Date: ....

↙ Reference the List on Page 39

Symptoms - Fill in the symptoms you are experiencing.

Symptoms:	Comments	Score
_____	_____	_____
_____	_____	_____
_____	_____	_____
_____	_____	_____
_____	_____	_____
_____	_____	_____
_____	_____	_____

Score symptoms from 0 (very low) to 5 (extreme)   **Total Score** _____

Activity - E.g. walking, weight exercise, classes   **Duration**

Type:

_____   _____

_____   _____

_____   _____

How do you feel overall?　Great | Good | Up & Down | Low

How did you sleep?　Great | Good | Poor | Hrs: ___

Diet - What did you eat today?

Did you have any of these phytoestrogenic foods today?

O Soy beans – edamame, tofu

O Peas and beans

O Lentils

O Seeds – flaxseed, sesame

O Fruits – banana, apple, orange

O Wholegrain and wheat bran

O Vegetables – cauliflower, broccoli, carrots, cabbage

O Berries and currants

O Other

See Page 17 for More Details

Total water intake (aim for 8 large glasses):

O　　O　　O　　O　　O　　O　　O　　O

If you could summarise today in 3 words, what would they be?

1.

2.

3.

Thrive
Day 28

Date: ....

Reference the List on Page 39

Symptoms - Fill in the symptoms you are experiencing.

Symptoms:	Comments	Score
_____	_____	_____
_____	_____	_____
_____	_____	_____
_____	_____	_____
_____	_____	_____
_____	_____	_____
_____	_____	_____

Score symptoms from 0 (very low) to 5 (extreme)　　　**Total Score** _____

Activity - E.g. walking, weight exercise, classes　　　**Duration**

Type:

_____　　_____

_____　　_____

_____

| How do you feel overall? | Great | Good | Up & Down | Low | How did you sleep? | Great | Good | Poor | Hrs: ___ |

Diet - What did you eat today?

Did you have any of these phytoestrogenic foods today?

O Soy beans – edamame, tofu

O Peas and beans

O Lentils

O Seeds – flaxseed, sesame

O Fruits – banana, apple, orange

O Wholegrain and wheat bran

O Vegetables – cauliflower, broccoli, carrots, cabbage

O Berries and currants

O Other

See Page 17 for More Details

Total water intake (aim for 8 large glasses):

O   O   O   O   O   O   O   O

If you could summarise today in 3 words, what would they be?

1.

2.

3.

❝I see menopause as the start of the the next fabulous phase of life. Now is a time to 'tune in' to our bodies and embrace this new chapter. I feel more myself and love my body more now, than ever before.❞

Kim Cattrall

The *Mirror* Exercise

The mirror is your best friend, after all – it's YOU! It may feel a bit silly at first, but when you see yourself in a mirror (or even shop window), give yourself a smile and a wave. Congratulate yourself – you are still here and you're stilling rocking!

Draw a picture of yourself smiling and waving in this mirror. Don't worry about your drawing skills, just make it cheerful and fun.

This exercise can be repeated as often as is needed.

Day 29

You have now completed a month, pop back to your local independent health store to discuss your progress.

Date: ....

Reference the List on Page 39

Symptoms:	Comments	Score
_____	_____	_____
_____	_____	_____
_____	_____	_____
_____	_____	_____
_____	_____	_____
_____	_____	_____
_____	_____	_____
_____	_____	_____

Score symptoms from 0 (very low) to 5 (extreme)　　　　**Total Score** _____

Activity - E.g. walking, weight exercise, classes　　　　**Duration**

Type:

_____　_____

_____　_____

_____　_____

| How do you feel overall? | Great \| Good \| Up & Down \| Low |
| How did you sleep? | Great \| Good \| Poor \| Hrs: ___ |

Diet - What did you eat today?

Did you have any of these phytoestrogenic foods today?

O Soy beans – edamame, tofu

O Peas and beans

O Lentils

O Seeds – flaxseed, sesame

O Fruits – banana, apple, orange

O Wholegrain and wheat bran

O Vegetables – cauliflower, broccoli, carrots, cabbage

O Berries and currants

O Other

See Page 17 for More Details

Total water intake (aim for 8 large glasses):

O   O   O   O   O   O   O   O

If you could summarise today in 3 words, what would they be?

1.

2.

3.

Thrive
Day 30

Date: ....

Reference the List on Page 39

Symptoms - Fill in the symptoms you are experiencing.		
Symptoms:	Comments	Score
_____	_____	_____
_____	_____	_____
_____	_____	_____
_____	_____	_____
_____	_____	_____
_____	_____	_____
_____	_____	_____
_____	_____	_____

Score symptoms from 0 (very low) to 5 (extreme)   **Total Score** _____

Activity - E.g. walking, weight exercise, classes	**Duration**
Type:	
_____	_____
_____	_____
_____	_____

| How do you feel overall? | Great | Good | Up & Down | Low | How did you sleep? | Great | Good | Poor | Hrs: ___ |

Diet - What did you eat today?

Did you have any of these phytoestrogenic foods today?

O Soy beans – edamame, tofu

O Peas and beans

O Lentils

O Seeds – flaxseed, sesame

O Fruits – banana, apple, orange

O Wholegrain and wheat bran

O Vegetables – cauliflower, broccoli, carrots, cabbage

O Berries and currants

O Other

See Page 17 for More Details

Total water intake (aim for 8 large glasses):

O   O   O   O   O   O   O   O

If you could summarise today in 3 words, what would they be?

1.

2.

3.

Thrive
Day 31

Date: ....

Reference the List on Page 39

Symptoms - Fill in the symptoms you are experiencing.		
Symptoms:	Comments	Score
_____	_____	_____
_____	_____	_____
_____	_____	_____
_____	_____	_____
_____	_____	_____
_____	_____	_____
_____	_____	_____

Score symptoms from 0 (very low) to 5 (extreme) **Total Score** _____

Activity - E.g. walking, weight exercise, classes	Duration
Type:	
_____	_____
_____	_____

How do you feel overall? Great | Good | Up & Down | Low

How did you sleep? Great | Good | Poor | Hrs: ____

Diet - What did you eat today?

Did you have any of these phytoestrogenic foods today?

O Soy beans – edamame, tofu

O Peas and beans

O Lentils

O Seeds – flaxseed, sesame

O Fruits – banana, apple, orange

O Wholegrain and wheat bran

O Vegetables – cauliflower, broccoli, carrots, cabbage

O Berries and currants

O Other

See Page 17 for More Details

Total water intake (aim for 8 large glasses):

O   O   O   O   O   O   O   O

If you could summarise today in 3 words, what would they be?

1.

2.

3.

Thrive
Day 32

Date: ....

Reference the List on Page 39

Symptoms - Fill in the symptoms you are experiencing.

Symptoms:	Comments	Score
_____	_____	_____
_____	_____	_____
_____	_____	_____
_____	_____	_____
_____	_____	_____
_____	_____	_____
_____	_____	_____

Score symptoms from 0 (very low) to 5 (extreme)   **Total Score** _____

Activity - E.g. walking, weight exercise, classes   **Duration**

Type:

_____   _____

_____   _____

_____   _____

| How do you feel overall? | Great | Good | Up & Down | Low | How did you sleep? | Great | Good | Poor | Hrs: ___ |

Diet - What did you eat today?

Did you have any of these phytoestrogenic foods today?

O Soy beans – edamame, tofu

O Peas and beans

O Lentils

O Seeds – flaxseed, sesame

O Fruits – banana, apple, orange

O Wholegrain and wheat bran

O Vegetables – cauliflower, broccoli, carrots, cabbage

O Berries and currants

O Other

See Page 17 for More Details

Total water intake (aim for 8 large glasses):

O   O   O   O   O   O   O   O

If you could summarise today in 3 words, what would they be?

1.

2.

3.

Thrive
Day 33

Date: ....

Reference the List on Page 39

Symptoms - Fill in the symptoms you are experiencing.

Symptoms:	Comments	Score
_____	_____	_____
_____	_____	_____
_____	_____	_____
_____	_____	_____
_____	_____	_____
_____	_____	_____
_____	_____	_____

Score symptoms from 0 (very low) to 5 (extreme)   **Total Score** _____

Activity - E.g. walking, weight exercise, classes   **Duration**

Type:

_____   _____

_____   _____

_____   _____

| How do you feel overall? | Great | Good | Up & Down | Low | How did you sleep? | Great | Good | Poor | Hrs: ___ |

Diet - What did you eat today?

Did you have any of these phytoestrogenic foods today?

O Soy beans – edamame, tofu

O Peas and beans

O Lentils

O Seeds – flaxseed, sesame

O Fruits – banana, apple, orange

O Wholegrain and wheat bran

O Vegetables – cauliflower, broccoli, carrots, cabbage

O Berries and currants

O Other

See Page 17 for More Details

Total water intake (aim for 8 large glasses):

O   O   O   O   O   O   O   O

If you could summarise today in 3 words, what would they be?

1.

2.

3.

Day 34

Date: ....

Reference the List on Page 39

Symptoms - Fill in the symptoms you are experiencing.

Symptoms:	Comments	Score

Score symptoms from 0 (very low) to 5 (extreme)   **Total Score** _____

Activity - E.g. walking, weight exercise, classes   **Duration**

Type:

How do you feel overall? Great | Good | Up & Down | Low

How did you sleep? Great | Good | Poor | Hrs: ____

Diet - What did you eat today?

Did you have any of these phytoestrogenic foods today?

O Soy beans – edamame, tofu

O Peas and beans

O Lentils

O Seeds – flaxseed, sesame

O Fruits – banana, apple, orange

O Wholegrain and wheat bran

O Vegetables – cauliflower, broccoli, carrots, cabbage

O Berries and currants

O Other

See Page 17 for More Details

Total water intake (aim for 8 large glasses):

O   O   O   O   O   O   O   O

If you could summarise today in 3 words, what would they be?

1.

2.

3.

Thrive
Day 35

Date: ....

Reference the List on Page 39

Symptoms - Fill in the symptoms you are experiencing.

Symptoms:	Comments	Score
_____	_____	_____
_____	_____	_____
_____	_____	_____
_____	_____	_____
_____	_____	_____
_____	_____	_____
_____	_____	_____

Score symptoms from 0 (very low) to 5 (extreme)　　　　**Total Score** _____

Activity - E.g. walking, weight exercise, classes　　　　**Duration**

Type:

_____　_____

_____　_____

_____　_____

How do you feel overall? Great | Good | Up & Down | Low

How did you sleep? Great | Good | Poor | Hrs: ___

Diet - What did you eat today?

Did you have any of these phytoestrogenic foods today?

O Soy beans – edamame, tofu

O Peas and beans

O Lentils

O Seeds – flaxseed, sesame

O Fruits – banana, apple, orange

O Wholegrain and wheat bran

O Vegetables – cauliflower, broccoli, carrots, cabbage

O Berries and currants

O Other

See Page 17 for More Details

Total water intake (aim for 8 large glasses):

O   O   O   O   O   O   O   O

If you could summarise today in 3 words, what would they be?

1.

2.

3.

Julie Walters

"If you deal with it in a healthy fashion then I think you come out the other side a better person. I've got so much more energy now than I ever had in my early 50s before the menopause."

The *Court Hearing* Exercise

If you find you are JUDGING yourself badly, write down 10 pieces of EVIDENCE where you have succeeded (for instance, I got up early today or I managed 1,000 steps more than yesterday, or perhaps I overcame something when I was a teenager).

1...

2...

3...

4...

5...

6...

7...

8...

9...

10...

This exercise can be repeated as often as is needed.

Thrive
Day 36

Date: ....

Reference the List on Page 39

Symptoms - Fill in the symptoms you are experiencing.

Symptoms:	Comments	Score
_____	_____	_____
_____	_____	_____
_____	_____	_____
_____	_____	_____
_____	_____	_____
_____	_____	_____
_____	_____	_____

Score symptoms from 0 (very low) to 5 (extreme)   **Total Score** _____

Activity - E.g. walking, weight exercise, classes   **Duration**

Type:

_____   _____

_____   _____

_____   _____

How do you feel overall? Great | Good | Up & Down | Low

How did you sleep? Great | Good | Poor | Hrs: ____

Diet - What did you eat today?

Did you have any of these phytoestrogenic foods today?

O Soy beans – edamame, tofu

O Peas and beans

O Lentils

O Seeds – flaxseed, sesame

O Fruits – banana, apple, orange

O Wholegrain and wheat bran

O Vegetables – cauliflower, broccoli, carrots, cabbage

O Berries and currants

O Other

See Page 17 for More Details

Total water intake (aim for 8 large glasses):

O   O   O   O   O   O   O   O

If you could summarise today in 3 words, what would they be?

1.

2.

3.

Thrive
Day 37

Date: ....

Reference the List on Page 39

Symptoms - Fill in the symptoms you are experiencing.

Symptoms:	Comments	Score
_____	_____	_____
_____	_____	_____
_____	_____	_____
_____	_____	_____
_____	_____	_____
_____	_____	_____
_____	_____	_____

Score symptoms from 0 (very low) to 5 (extreme)　　　**Total Score** _____

Activity - E.g. walking, weight exercise, classes　　　**Duration**

Type:

_____　　_____

_____　　_____

_____　　_____

How do you feel overall? Great | Good | Up & Down | Low

How did you sleep? Great | Good | Poor | Hrs: ___

Diet - What did you eat today?

Did you have any of these phytoestrogenic foods today?

O Soy beans – edamame, tofu

O Peas and beans

O Lentils

O Seeds – flaxseed, sesame

O Fruits – banana, apple, orange

O Wholegrain and wheat bran

O Vegetables – cauliflower, broccoli, carrots, cabbage

O Berries and currants

O Other

See Page 17 for More Details

Total water intake (aim for 8 large glasses):

O   O   O   O   O   O   O   O

If you could summarise today in 3 words, what would they be?

1.

2.

3.

Thrive
Day 38

Date: ....

Reference the List on Page 39

Symptoms - Fill in the symptoms you are experiencing.

Symptoms:	Comments	Score

Score symptoms from 0 (very low) to 5 (extreme)   **Total Score** _____

Activity - E.g. walking, weight exercise, classes   **Duration**

Type:

| How do you feel overall? | Great \| Good \| Up & Down \| Low | How did you sleep? | Great \| Good \| Poor \| Hrs: ___ |

Diet - What did you eat today?

Did you have any of these phytoestrogenic foods today?

O Soy beans – edamame, tofu

O Peas and beans

O Lentils

O Seeds – flaxseed, sesame

O Fruits – banana, apple, orange

O Wholegrain and wheat bran

O Vegetables – cauliflower, broccoli, carrots, cabbage

O Berries and currants

O Other

Total water intake (aim for 8 large glasses):

O O O O O O O O

See Page 17 for More Details

If you could summarise today in 3 words, what would they be?

1.

2.

3.

Thrive
Day 39

Date: ....

Reference the List on Page 39

Symptoms - Fill in the symptoms you are experiencing.		
Symptoms:	Comments	Score
_____	_____	_____
_____	_____	_____
_____	_____	_____
_____	_____	_____
_____	_____	_____
_____	_____	_____
_____	_____	_____
_____	_____	_____

Score symptoms from 0 (very low) to 5 (extreme) **Total Score** _____

Activity - E.g. walking, weight exercise, classes	**Duration**
Type:	
_____	_____
_____	_____
_____	_____

How do you feel overall? Great | Good | Up & Down | Low

How did you sleep? Great | Good | Poor | Hrs: ____

Diet - What did you eat today?

Did you have any of these phytoestrogenic foods today?

O Soy beans – edamame, tofu

O Peas and beans

O Lentils

O Seeds – flaxseed, sesame

O Fruits – banana, apple, orange

O Wholegrain and wheat bran

O Vegetables – cauliflower, broccoli, carrots, cabbage

O Berries and currants

O Other

See Page 17 for More Details

Total water intake (aim for 8 large glasses):

O   O   O   O   O   O   O   O

If you could summarise today in 3 words, what would they be?

1.

2.

3.

Thrive
Day 40

Date: ....

Reference the List on Page 39

Symptoms - Fill in the symptoms you are experiencing.

Symptoms:	Comments	Score
_____	_____	____
_____	_____	____
_____	_____	____
_____	_____	____
_____	_____	____
_____	_____	____
_____	_____	____
_____	_____	____

Score symptoms from 0 (very low) to 5 (extreme)   **Total Score** _____

Activity - E.g. walking, weight exercise, classes   **Duration**

Type:

_____   _____

_____   _____

_____   _____

| How do you feel overall? | Great \| Good \| Up & Down \| Low | How did you sleep? | Great \| Good \| Poor \| Hrs: ____ |

Diet - What did you eat today?

Did you have any of these phytoestrogenic foods today?

O Soy beans – edamame, tofu

O Peas and beans

O Lentils

O Seeds – flaxseed, sesame

O Fruits – banana, apple, orange

O Wholegrain and wheat bran

O Vegetables – cauliflower, broccoli, carrots, cabbage

O Berries and currants

O Other

Total water intake (aim for 8 large glasses):

O   O   O   O   O   O   O   O

See Page 17 for More Details

If you could summarise today in 3 words, what would they be?

1.

2.

3.

Thrive
Day 41

Date: ....

Reference the List on Page 39

Symptoms - Fill in the symptoms you are experiencing.

Symptoms:	Comments	Score
_____	_____	_____
_____	_____	_____
_____	_____	_____
_____	_____	_____
_____	_____	_____
_____	_____	_____
_____	_____	_____

Score symptoms from 0 (very low) to 5 (extreme)   **Total Score** _____

Activity - E.g. walking, weight exercise, classes   **Duration**

Type:
_____ _____

_____ _____

_____ _____

| How do you feel overall? | Great \| Good \| Up & Down \| Low | How did you sleep? | Great \| Good \| Poor \| Hrs: ___ |

Diet - What did you eat today?

Did you have any of these phytoestrogenic foods today?

O Soy beans – edamame, tofu

O Peas and beans

O Lentils

O Seeds – flaxseed, sesame

O Fruits – banana, apple, orange

O Wholegrain and wheat bran

O Vegetables – cauliflower, broccoli, carrots, cabbage

O Berries and currants

O Other

Total water intake (aim for 8 large glasses):

O   O   O   O   O   O   O   O

See Page 17 for More Details

If you could summarise today in 3 words, what would they be?

1.

2.

3.

Thrive
Day 42

Date: ....

Reference the List on Page 39

Symptoms - Fill in the symptoms you are experiencing.		
Symptoms:	Comments	Score
_____	_____	_____
_____	_____	_____
_____	_____	_____
_____	_____	_____
_____	_____	_____
_____	_____	_____
_____	_____	_____

Score symptoms from 0 (very low) to 5 (extreme)   **Total Score** _____

Activity - E.g. walking, weight exercise, classes	Duration
Type:	
_____	_____
_____	_____
_____	_____

How do you feel overall? Great | Good | Up & Down | Low

How did you sleep? Great | Good | Poor | Hrs: ___

Diet - What did you eat today?

Did you have any of these phytoestrogenic foods today?

O Soy beans – edamame, tofu

O Peas and beans

O Lentils

O Seeds – flaxseed, sesame

O Fruits – banana, apple, orange

O Wholegrain and wheat bran

O Vegetables – cauliflower, broccoli, carrots, cabbage

O Berries and currants

O Other

Total water intake (aim for 8 large glasses):

O   O   O   O   O   O   O   O

See Page 17 for More Details

If you could summarise today in 3 words, what would they be?

1.

2.

3.

"How hideous for women of our mothers' generation, because - while me and my girlfriends will talk about **everything under the sun**, including the menopause - it was something they didn't discuss. They must have felt so lonely and embarrassed all the time. The more open we are about it, the less of a taboo it will become."

Amanda Redman

The *Future Feelings* Exercise

Imagine what you most desire to achieve in the next year. What will it feel like to exceed your expectations? Write down how you will feel when you reach that goal...

This exercise can be repeated as often as is needed.

Thrive
Day 43

Date: ....

Reference the List on Page 39

Symptoms - Fill in the symptoms you are experiencing.

Symptoms:	Comments	Score
_____	_____	_____
_____	_____	_____
_____	_____	_____
_____	_____	_____
_____	_____	_____
_____	_____	_____
_____	_____	_____

Score symptoms from 0 (very low) to 5 (extreme)   **Total Score** _____

Activity - E.g. walking, weight exercise, classes   **Duration**

Type:

_____   _____

_____   _____

_____   _____

| How do you feel overall? | Great | Good | Up & Down | Low | | How did you sleep? | Great | Good | Poor | Hrs: ___ |

Diet - What did you eat today?

Did you have any of these phytoestrogenic foods today?

O Soy beans – edamame, tofu

O Peas and beans

O Lentils

O Seeds – flaxseed, sesame

O Fruits – banana, apple, orange

O Wholegrain and wheat bran

O Vegetables – cauliflower, broccoli, carrots, cabbage

O Berries and currants

O Other

See Page 17 for More Details

Total water intake (aim for 8 large glasses):

O   O   O   O   O   O   O   O

If you could summarise today in 3 words, what would they be?

1.

2.

3.

Day 44

Date: ....

Reference the List on Page 39

Symptoms - Fill in the symptoms you are experiencing.

Symptoms:	Comments	Score
_____	_____	_____
_____	_____	_____
_____	_____	_____
_____	_____	_____
_____	_____	_____
_____	_____	_____
_____	_____	_____

Score symptoms from 0 (very low) to 5 (extreme)   **Total Score** _____

Activity - E.g. walking, weight exercise, classes   **Duration**

Type:		
_____	_____	_____
_____	_____	_____
_____	_____	_____

| How do you feel overall? | Great | Good | Up & Down | Low | How did you sleep? | Great | Good | Poor | Hrs: ____ |

Diet - What did you eat today?

Did you have any of these phytoestrogenic foods today?

O Soy beans – edamame, tofu

O Peas and beans

O Lentils

O Seeds – flaxseed, sesame

O Fruits – banana, apple, orange

O Wholegrain and wheat bran

O Vegetables – cauliflower, broccoli, carrots, cabbage

O Berries and currants

O Other

See Page 17 for More Details

Total water intake (aim for 8 large glasses):

O O O O O O O O

If you could summarise today in 3 words, what would they be?

1.

2.

3.

Thrive
Day 45

Date: ....

Reference the List on Page 39

Symptoms - Fill in the symptoms you are experiencing.

Symptoms:	Comments	Score
_____	_____	_____
_____	_____	_____
_____	_____	_____
_____	_____	_____
_____	_____	_____
_____	_____	_____
_____	_____	_____

Score symptoms from 0 (very low) to 5 (extreme)   **Total Score** _____

Activity - E.g. walking, weight exercise, classes   **Duration**

Type:

_____   _____

_____   _____

_____   _____

| How do you feel overall? | Great | Good | Up & Down | Low | How did you sleep? | Great | Good | Poor | Hrs: ___ |

Diet - What did you eat today?

Did you have any of these phytoestrogenic foods today?

O Soy beans – edamame, tofu

O Peas and beans

O Lentils

O Seeds – flaxseed, sesame

O Fruits – banana, apple, orange

O Wholegrain and wheat bran

O Vegetables – cauliflower, broccoli, carrots, cabbage

O Berries and currants

O Other

Total water intake (aim for 8 large glasses):

O   O   O   O   O   O   O   O

See Page 17 for More Details

If you could summarise today in 3 words, what would they be?

1.

2.

3.

Thrive
Day 46

Date: ....

Reference the List on Page 39

Symptoms - Fill in the symptoms you are experiencing.		
Symptoms:	Comments	Score
_____	_____	_____
_____	_____	_____
_____	_____	_____
_____	_____	_____
_____	_____	_____
_____	_____	_____
_____	_____	_____
_____	_____	_____

Score symptoms from 0 (very low) to 5 (extreme)   **Total Score** _____

Activity - E.g. walking, weight exercise, classes	Duration
Type:	
_____	_____
_____	_____
_____	_____

| How do you feel overall? | Great \| Good \| Up & Down \| Low | How did you sleep? | Great \| Good \| Poor \| Hrs: ___ |

Diet - What did you eat today?

Did you have any of these phytoestrogenic foods today?

O Soy beans – edamame, tofu

O Peas and beans

O Lentils

O Seeds – flaxseed, sesame

O Fruits – banana, apple, orange

O Wholegrain and wheat bran

O Vegetables – cauliflower, broccoli, carrots, cabbage

O Berries and currants

O Other

Total water intake (aim for 8 large glasses):

O   O   O   O   O   O   O   O

See Page 17 for More Details

If you could summarise today in 3 words, what would they be?

1.

2.

3.

Thrive
Day 47

Date: ....

Reference the List on Page 39

Symptoms - Fill in the symptoms you are experiencing.		
Symptoms:	Comments	Score
_____	_____	_____
_____	_____	_____
_____	_____	_____
_____	_____	_____
_____	_____	_____
_____	_____	_____
_____	_____	_____

Score symptoms from 0 (very low) to 5 (extreme)   **Total Score** _____

Activity - E.g. walking, weight exercise, classes	**Duration**
Type:	
_____	_____
_____	_____
_____	_____

How do you feel overall?   Great | Good | Up & Down | Low

How did you sleep?   Great | Good | Poor | Hrs: ____

Diet - What did you eat today?

Did you have any of these phytoestrogenic foods today?

O Soy beans – edamame, tofu

O Peas and beans

O Lentils

O Seeds – flaxseed, sesame

O Fruits – banana, apple, orange

O Wholegrain and wheat bran

O Vegetables – cauliflower, broccoli, carrots, cabbage

O Berries and currants

O Other

See Page 17 for More Details

Total water intake (aim for 8 large glasses):

O   O   O   O   O   O   O   O

If you could summarise today in 3 words, what would they be?

1.

2.

3.

Thrive
Day 48

Date: ....

Reference the List on Page 39

Symptoms - Fill in the symptoms you are experiencing.

Symptoms:	Comments	Score
_____	_____	_____
_____	_____	_____
_____	_____	_____
_____	_____	_____
_____	_____	_____
_____	_____	_____
_____	_____	_____

Score symptoms from 0 (very low) to 5 (extreme)   **Total Score** _____

Activity - E.g. walking, weight exercise, classes   **Duration**

Type:

_____   _____

_____   _____

_____   _____

How do you feel overall? Great | Good | Up & Down | Low

How did you sleep? Great | Good | Poor | Hrs: ____

Diet - What did you eat today?

Did you have any of these phytoestrogenic foods today?

O Soy beans – edamame, tofu

O Peas and beans

O Lentils

O Seeds – flaxseed, sesame

O Fruits – banana, apple, orange

O Wholegrain and wheat bran

O Vegetables – cauliflower, broccoli, carrots, cabbage

O Berries and currants

O Other

Total water intake (aim for 8 large glasses):

O   O   O   O   O   O   O   O

See Page 17 for More Details

If you could summarise today in 3 words, what would they be?

1.

2.

3.

Thrive
Day 49

Date: ....

Reference the List on Page 39

Symptoms - Fill in the symptoms you are experiencing.		
Symptoms:	Comments	Score
_____	_____	_____
_____	_____	_____
_____	_____	_____
_____	_____	_____
_____	_____	_____
_____	_____	_____
_____	_____	_____

Score symptoms from 0 (very low) to 5 (extreme)   **Total Score** _____

Activity - E.g. walking, weight exercise, classes	Duration
Type:	
_____	_____
_____	_____
_____	_____

| How do you feel overall? | Great \| Good \| Up & Down \| Low | How did you sleep? | Great \| Good \| Poor \| Hrs: ____ |

Diet - What did you eat today?

Did you have any of these phytoestrogenic foods today?

O Soy beans – edamame, tofu

O Peas and beans

O Lentils

O Seeds – flaxseed, sesame

O Fruits – banana, apple, orange

O Wholegrain and wheat bran

O Vegetables – cauliflower, broccoli, carrots, cabbage

O Berries and currants

O Other

Total water intake (aim for 8 large glasses):

O   O   O   O   O   O   O   O

See Page 17 for More Details

If you could summarise today in 3 words, what would they be?

1.

2.

3.

Sally Field

" I so believe that older women have tremendous value to their families, their community, their country, the world. "

The *I Am* Exercise

Our inner voice can be our hardest critic. Practice positive affirmations. Write down 10 positive statements about yourself and repeat them 5 times daily.

I am ...

I am ...

I am ...

I am ...

I am ...

I am ...

I am ...

I am ...

I am ...

I am ...

This exercise can be repeated as often as is needed.

Thrive
Day 50

Date: ....

Reference the List on Page 39

Symptoms - Fill in the symptoms you are experiencing.

Symptoms:	Comments	Score
_____	_____	_____
_____	_____	_____
_____	_____	_____
_____	_____	_____
_____	_____	_____
_____	_____	_____
_____	_____	_____

Score symptoms from 0 (very low) to 5 (extreme)   **Total Score** _____

Activity - E.g. walking, weight exercise, classes   **Duration**

Type:
_____   _____
_____   _____
_____   _____

| How do you feel overall? | Great | Good | Up & Down | Low | How did you sleep? | Great | Good | Poor | Hrs: ____ |

Diet - What did you eat today?

Did you have any of these phytoestrogenic foods today?

O Soy beans – edamame, tofu

O Peas and beans

O Lentils

O Seeds – flaxseed, sesame

O Fruits – banana, apple, orange

O Wholegrain and wheat bran

O Vegetables – cauliflower, broccoli, carrots, cabbage

O Berries and currants

O Other

See Page 17 for More Details

Total water intake (aim for 8 large glasses):

O   O   O   O   O   O   O   O

If you could summarise today in 3 words, what would they be?

1.

2.

3.

Thrive
Day 51

Date: ....

✓ Reference the List on Page 39

Symptoms - Fill in the symptoms you are experiencing.		
Symptoms:	Comments	Score
_____	_____	_____
_____	_____	_____
_____	_____	_____
_____	_____	_____
_____	_____	_____
_____	_____	_____
_____	_____	_____

Score symptoms from 0 (very low) to 5 (extreme)   **Total Score** _____

Activity - E.g. walking, weight exercise, classes	Duration
Type:	
_____	_____
_____	_____
_____	_____

How do you feel overall? Great | Good | Up & Down | Low

How did you sleep? Great | Good | Poor | Hrs: ___

Diet - What did you eat today?

Did you have any of these phytoestrogenic foods today?

O Soy beans – edamame, tofu

O Peas and beans

O Lentils

O Seeds – flaxseed, sesame

O Fruits – banana, apple, orange

O Wholegrain and wheat bran

O Vegetables – cauliflower, broccoli, carrots, cabbage

O Berries and currants

O Other

See Page 17 for More Details

Total water intake (aim for 8 large glasses):

O   O   O   O   O   O   O   O

If you could summarise today in 3 words, what would they be?

1.   **2.**   **3.**

Thrive
Day 52

Date: ....

↙ Reference the List on Page 39

Symptoms - Fill in the symptoms you are experiencing.

Symptoms:	Comments	Score
_____	_____	_____
_____	_____	_____
_____	_____	_____
_____	_____	_____
_____	_____	_____
_____	_____	_____
_____	_____	_____

Score symptoms from 0 (very low) to 5 (extreme)   **Total Score** _____

Activity - E.g. walking, weight exercise, classes   **Duration**

Type:

_____   _____

_____   _____

_____   _____

| How do you feel overall? | Great \| Good \| Up & Down \| Low | How did you sleep? | Great \| Good \| Poor \| Hrs: ____ |

Diet - What did you eat today?

Did you have any of these phytoestrogenic foods today?

O Soy beans – edamame, tofu

O Peas and beans

O Lentils

O Seeds – flaxseed, sesame

O Fruits – banana, apple, orange

O Wholegrain and wheat bran

O Vegetables – cauliflower, broccoli, carrots, cabbage

O Berries and currants

O Other

Total water intake (aim for 8 large glasses):

O   O   O   O   O   O   O   O

See Page 17 for More Details

If you could summarise today in 3 words, what would they be?

1.

2.

3.

Thrive
Day 53

Date: ....

Reference the List on Page 39

Symptoms - Fill in the symptoms you are experiencing.

Symptoms:	Comments	Score
_____	_____	___
_____	_____	___
_____	_____	___
_____	_____	___
_____	_____	___
_____	_____	___
_____	_____	___
_____	_____	___

Score symptoms from 0 (very low) to 5 (extreme)　　　　**Total Score** _____

Activity - E.g. walking, weight exercise, classes　　　　**Duration**

Type:

_____　　_____

_____　　_____

_____　　_____

| How do you feel overall? | Great | Good | Up & Down | Low | How did you sleep? | Great | Good | Poor | Hrs: ____ |

Diet - What did you eat today?

Did you have any of these phytoestrogenic foods today?

O Soy beans – edamame, tofu

O Peas and beans

O Lentils

O Seeds – flaxseed, sesame

O Fruits – banana, apple, orange

O Wholegrain and wheat bran

O Vegetables – cauliflower, broccoli, carrots, cabbage

O Berries and currants

O Other

Total water intake (aim for 8 large glasses):

O   O   O   O   O   O   O   O

See Page 17 for More Details

If you could summarise today in 3 words, what would they be?

1.

2.

3.

Day 54

Date: ....

Reference the List on Page 39

Symptoms - Fill in the symptoms you are experiencing.		
Symptoms:	Comments	Score
_____	_____	_____
_____	_____	_____
_____	_____	_____
_____	_____	_____
_____	_____	_____
_____	_____	_____
_____	_____	_____

Score symptoms from 0 (very low) to 5 (extreme) **Total Score** _____

Activity - E.g. walking, weight exercise, classes	**Duration**
Type:	
_____	_____
_____	_____
_____	_____

| How do you feel overall? | Great | Good | Up & Down | Low | How did you sleep? | Great | Good | Poor | Hrs: ___ |

Diet - What did you eat today?

Did you have any of these phytoestrogenic foods today?

O Soy beans – edamame, tofu

O Peas and beans

O Lentils

O Seeds – flaxseed, sesame

O Fruits – banana, apple, orange

O Wholegrain and wheat bran

O Vegetables – cauliflower, broccoli, carrots, cabbage

O Berries and currants

O Other

Total water intake (aim for 8 large glasses):

O   O   O   O   O   O   O   O

See Page 17 for More Details

If you could summarise today in 3 words, what would they be?

1.

2.

3.

Thrive
Day 55

Date: ....

↙ Reference the List on Page 39

Symptoms - Fill in the symptoms you are experiencing.

Symptoms:	Comments	Score
_____	_____	_____
_____	_____	_____
_____	_____	_____
_____	_____	_____
_____	_____	_____
_____	_____	_____
_____	_____	_____

Score symptoms from 0 (very low) to 5 (extreme)   **Total Score** _____

Activity - E.g. walking, weight exercise, classes   **Duration**

Type:

_____   _____

_____   _____

_____   _____

How do you feel overall?	Great	Good	Up & Down	Low

How did you sleep?	Great	Good	Poor	Hrs: ____

Diet - What did you eat today?

Did you have any of these phytoestrogenic foods today?

O Soy beans – edamame, tofu

O Peas and beans

O Lentils

O Seeds – flaxseed, sesame

O Fruits – banana, apple, orange

O Wholegrain and wheat bran

O Vegetables – cauliflower, broccoli, carrots, cabbage

O Berries and currants

O Other

Total water intake (aim for 8 large glasses):

O   O   O   O   O   O   O   O

See Page 17 for More Details

If you could summarise today in 3 words, what would they be?

1.

2.

3.

Thrive
Day 56

Date: ....

Reference the List on Page 39

Symptoms - Fill in the symptoms you are experiencing.

Symptoms:	Comments	Score
_____	_____	_____
_____	_____	_____
_____	_____	_____
_____	_____	_____
_____	_____	_____
_____	_____	_____
_____	_____	_____
_____	_____	_____

Score symptoms from 0 (very low) to 5 (extreme)   **Total Score** _____

Activity - E.g. walking, weight exercise, classes   **Duration**

Type:

_____ _____

_____ _____

_____ _____

How do you feel overall?   Great | Good | Up & Down | Low

How did you sleep?   Great | Good | Poor | Hrs: ____

Diet - What did you eat today?

Did you have any of these phytoestrogenic foods today?

O Soy beans – edamame, tofu

O Peas and beans

O Lentils

O Seeds – flaxseed, sesame

O Fruits – banana, apple, orange

O Wholegrain and wheat bran

O Vegetables – cauliflower, broccoli, carrots, cabbage

O Berries and currants

O Other

See Page 17 for More Details

Total water intake (aim for 8 large glasses):

O   O   O   O   O   O   O   O

If you could summarise today in 3 words, what would they be?

1.

2.

3.

"I do think that when it comes to ageing, we're held to a **different standard** than men. Some guy said to me: 'Don't you think you're too old to sing rock 'n' roll?' I said: 'You'd better check with Mick Jagger'."

Cher

The *Gratitude* Exercise

When feeling sad, lonely or overwhelmed, identifying the things you are grateful for can help. List 5 things you are grateful for that happened in the last 24 hours.

1...

2...

3...

4...

5...

This exercise can be repeated as often as is needed.

Thrive
Day 57

You are now two months into your personalised program and making great progress. Check in with your healthcare advisor if needed.

Date: ....

Reference the List on Page 39

Symptoms - Fill in the symptoms you are experiencing.		
Symptoms:	Comments	Score
_____	_____	_____
_____	_____	_____
_____	_____	_____
_____	_____	_____
_____	_____	_____
_____	_____	_____
_____	_____	_____
_____	_____	_____

Score symptoms from 0 (very low) to 5 (extreme) **Total Score** _____

Activity - E.g. walking, weight exercise, classes	**Duration**
Type:	
_____	_____
_____	_____
_____	_____

| How do you feel overall? | Great │ Good │ Up & Down │ Low | How did you sleep? | Great │ Good │ Poor │ Hrs: ____ |

Diet - What did you eat today?

Did you have any of these phytoestrogenic foods today?

O Soy beans – edamame, tofu

O Peas and beans

O Lentils

O Seeds – flaxseed, sesame

O Fruits – banana, apple, orange

O Wholegrain and wheat bran

O Vegetables – cauliflower, broccoli, carrots, cabbage

O Berries and currants

O Other

Total water intake (aim for 8 large glasses):

O   O   O   O   O   O   O   O

See Page 17 for More Details

If you could summarise today in 3 words, what would they be?

1.

2.

3.

Thrive
Day 58

Date: ....

Reference the List on Page 39

Symptoms - Fill in the symptoms you are experiencing.

Symptoms:	Comments	Score
_____	_____	_____
_____	_____	_____
_____	_____	_____
_____	_____	_____
_____	_____	_____
_____	_____	_____
_____	_____	_____

Score symptoms from 0 (very low) to 5 (extreme)   **Total Score** _____

Activity - E.g. walking, weight exercise, classes   **Duration**

Type:

_____   _____

_____   _____

_____   _____

| How do you feel overall? | Great | Good | Up & Down | Low | How did you sleep? | Great | Good | Poor | Hrs: ___ |

Diet - What did you eat today?

Did you have any of these phytoestrogenic foods today?

O Soy beans – edamame, tofu

O Peas and beans

O Lentils

O Seeds – flaxseed, sesame

O Fruits – banana, apple, orange

O Wholegrain and wheat bran

O Vegetables – cauliflower, broccoli, carrots, cabbage

O Berries and currants

O Other

Total water intake (aim for 8 large glasses):

O   O   O   O   O   O   O   O

See Page 17 for More Details

If you could summarise today in 3 words, what would they be?

1.

2.

3.

Thrive
Day 59

Date: ....

Reference the List on Page 39

Symptoms - Fill in the symptoms you are experiencing.		
Symptoms:	Comments	Score

Score symptoms from 0 (very low) to 5 (extreme)   **Total Score** _____

Activity - E.g. walking, weight exercise, classes	Duration
Type:	

| How do you feel overall? | Great \| Good \| Up & Down \| Low | How did you sleep? | Great \| Good \| Poor \| Hrs: ___ |

Diet - What did you eat today?

Did you have any of these phytoestrogenic foods today?

O Soy beans – edamame, tofu

O Peas and beans

O Lentils

O Seeds – flaxseed, sesame

O Fruits – banana, apple, orange

O Wholegrain and wheat bran

O Vegetables – cauliflower, broccoli, carrots, cabbage

O Berries and currants

O Other

Total water intake (aim for 8 large glasses):

O   O   O   O   O   O   O   O

See Page 17 for More Details

If you could summarise today in 3 words, what would they be?

1.   **2.**   **3.**

Thrive
Day 60

Date: ....

Reference the List on Page 39

Symptoms - Fill in the symptoms you are experiencing.

Symptoms:	Comments	Score
_____	_____	____
_____	_____	____
_____	_____	____
_____	_____	____
_____	_____	____
_____	_____	____
_____	_____	____

Score symptoms from 0 (very low) to 5 (extreme) **Total Score** _____

Activity - E.g. walking, weight exercise, classes **Duration**

Type:

_____ _____

_____ _____

_____ _____

| How do you feel overall? | Great | Good | Up & Down | Low | How did you sleep? | Great | Good | Poor | Hrs: ____ |

Diet - What did you eat today?

Did you have any of these phytoestrogenic foods today?

O Soy beans – edamame, tofu

O Peas and beans

O Lentils

O Seeds – flaxseed, sesame

O Fruits – banana, apple, orange

O Wholegrain and wheat bran

O Vegetables – cauliflower, broccoli, carrots, cabbage

O Berries and currants

O Other

See Page 17 for More Details

Total water intake (aim for 8 large glasses):

O   O   O   O   O   O   O   O

If you could summarise today in 3 words, what would they be?

1.

2.

3.

Thrive
Day 61

Date: ....

Reference the List on Page 39

Symptoms - Fill in the symptoms you are experiencing.

Symptoms:	Comments	Score
_____	_____	____
_____	_____	____
_____	_____	____
_____	_____	____
_____	_____	____
_____	_____	____
_____	_____	____
_____	_____	____

Score symptoms from 0 (very low) to 5 (extreme)　　**Total Score** _____

Activity - E.g. walking, weight exercise, classes　　**Duration**

Type:

_____ _____

_____ _____

_____ _____

How do you feel overall?   Great | Good | Up & Down | Low

How did you sleep?   Great | Good | Poor | Hrs: ____

Diet - What did you eat today?

Did you have any of these phytoestrogenic foods today?

O Soy beans – edamame, tofu

O Peas and beans

O Lentils

O Seeds – flaxseed, sesame

O Fruits – banana, apple, orange

O Wholegrain and wheat bran

O Vegetables – cauliflower, broccoli, carrots, cabbage

O Berries and currants

O Other

Total water intake (aim for 8 large glasses):

O   O   O   O   O   O   O   O

See Page 17 for More Details

If you could summarise today in 3 words, what would they be?

1.

2.

3.

Thrive
Day 62

Date: ....

Reference the List on Page 39

Symptoms - Fill in the symptoms you are experiencing.

Symptoms:	Comments	Score
_____	_____	_____
_____	_____	_____
_____	_____	_____
_____	_____	_____
_____	_____	_____
_____	_____	_____
_____	_____	_____

Score symptoms from 0 (very low) to 5 (extreme)   **Total Score** _____

Activity - E.g. walking, weight exercise, classes   **Duration**

Type:

_____   _____

_____   _____

_____

| How do you feel overall? | Great | Good | Up & Down | Low | How did you sleep? | Great | Good | Poor | Hrs: ___ |

Diet - What did you eat today?

Did you have any of these phytoestrogenic foods today?

O Soy beans – edamame, tofu

O Peas and beans

O Lentils

O Seeds – flaxseed, sesame

O Fruits – banana, apple, orange

O Wholegrain and wheat bran

O Vegetables – cauliflower, broccoli, carrots, cabbage

O Berries and currants

O Other

Total water intake (aim for 8 large glasses):

O   O   O   O   O   O   O   O

See Page 17 for More Details

If you could summarise today in 3 words, what would they be?

1.

2.

3.

Thrive
Day 63

Date: ....

↙ Reference the List on Page 39

Symptoms - Fill in the symptoms you are experiencing.

Symptoms:	Comments	Score
_____	_____	_____
_____	_____	_____
_____	_____	_____
_____	_____	_____
_____	_____	_____
_____	_____	_____
_____	_____	_____
_____	_____	_____

Score symptoms from 0 (very low) to 5 (extreme)   **Total Score** _____

Activity - E.g. walking, weight exercise, classes   **Duration**

Type:
_____   _____

_____   _____

_____   _____

| How do you feel overall? | Great | Good | Up & Down | Low | How did you sleep? | Great | Good | Poor | Hrs: ____ |

Diet - What did you eat today?

Did you have any of these phytoestrogenic foods today?

O Soy beans – edamame, tofu

O Peas and beans

O Lentils

O Seeds – flaxseed, sesame

O Fruits – banana, apple, orange

O Wholegrain and wheat bran

O Vegetables – cauliflower, broccoli, carrots, cabbage

O Berries and currants

O Other

See Page 17 for More Details

Total water intake (aim for 8 large glasses):

O   O   O   O   O   O   O   O

If you could summarise today in 3 words, what would they be?

1.   2.   3.

Suzanne Somers

"One thing I love about ageing – and I do love ageing – I've got a wisdom that no young person can buy. You earn it."

The Yes/No Exercise

Self-care requires the ability to follow your heart and say yes or no appropriately.

Describe a recent occasion when you wish you had said NO instead of YES.

Describe a recent occasion when you wish you had said YES instead of NO.

Said No...

Said Yes...

Said No...

Said Yes...

Said No...

Said Yes...

Said No...

Said Yes...

Said No...

Said Yes...

This exercise can be repeated as often as is needed.

Thrive
Day 64

Date: ....

↙ *Reference the List on Page 39*

Symptoms - Fill in the symptoms you are experiencing.

Symptoms:	Comments	Score
_____	_____	_____
_____	_____	_____
_____	_____	_____
_____	_____	_____
_____	_____	_____
_____	_____	_____
_____	_____	_____
_____	_____	_____

Score symptoms from 0 (very low) to 5 (extreme)   **Total Score** _____

Activity - E.g. walking, weight exercise, classes   **Duration**

Type:

_____   _____

_____   _____

_____   _____

| How do you feel overall? | Great | Good | Up & Down | Low | How did you sleep? | Great | Good | Poor | Hrs: ___ |

Diet - What did you eat today?

Did you have any of these phytoestrogenic foods today?

O Soy beans – edamame, tofu

O Peas and beans

O Lentils

O Seeds – flaxseed, sesame

O Fruits – banana, apple, orange

O Wholegrain and wheat bran

O Vegetables – cauliflower, broccoli, carrots, cabbage

O Berries and currants

O Other

Total water intake (aim for 8 large glasses):

O   O   O   O   O   O   O   O

See Page 17 for More Details

If you could summarise today in 3 words, what would they be?

1.

2.

3.

Thrive
Day 65

Date: ....

Reference the List on Page 39

Symptoms - Fill in the symptoms you are experiencing.

Symptoms:	Comments	Score
_____	_____	_____
_____	_____	_____
_____	_____	_____
_____	_____	_____
_____	_____	_____
_____	_____	_____
_____	_____	_____

Score symptoms from 0 (very low) to 5 (extreme)   **Total Score** _____

Activity - E.g. walking, weight exercise, classes   **Duration**

Type:

_____   _____

_____

_____

How do you feel overall? Great | Good | Up & Down | Low

How did you sleep? Great | Good | Poor | Hrs: ____

Diet - What did you eat today?

Did you have any of these phytoestrogenic foods today?

O Soy beans – edamame, tofu

O Peas and beans

O Lentils

O Seeds – flaxseed, sesame

O Fruits – banana, apple, orange

O Wholegrain and wheat bran

O Vegetables – cauliflower, broccoli, carrots, cabbage

O Berries and currants

O Other

See Page 17 for More Details

Total water intake (aim for 8 large glasses):

O   O   O   O   O   O   O   O

If you could summarise today in 3 words, what would they be?

1.   2.   3.

Thrive
Day 66

Date: ....

Reference the List on Page 39

Symptoms - Fill in the symptoms you are experiencing.		
Symptoms:	Comments	Score
_____	_____	_____
_____	_____	_____
_____	_____	_____
_____	_____	_____
_____	_____	_____
_____	_____	_____
_____	_____	_____

Score symptoms from 0 (very low) to 5 (extreme)   **Total Score** _____

Activity - E.g. walking, weight exercise, classes	Duration
Type:	
_____	_____
_____	_____
_____	_____

| How do you feel overall? | Great | Good | Up & Down | Low | How did you sleep? | Great | Good | Poor | Hrs: ___ |

Diet - What did you eat today?

Did you have any of these phytoestrogenic foods today?

O Soy beans – edamame, tofu

O Peas and beans

O Lentils

O Seeds – flaxseed, sesame

O Fruits – banana, apple, orange

O Wholegrain and wheat bran

O Vegetables – cauliflower, broccoli, carrots, cabbage

O Berries and currants

O Other

See Page 17
for More Details

Total water intake (aim for 8 large glasses):

O   O   O   O   O   O   O   O

If you could summarise today in 3 words, what would they be?

1.

2.

3.

Thrive
Day 67

Date: ....

Reference the List on Page 39

Symptoms - Fill in the symptoms you are experiencing.

Symptoms:	Comments	Score
_____	_____	____
_____	_____	____
_____	_____	____
_____	_____	____
_____	_____	____
_____	_____	____
_____	_____	____

Score symptoms from 0 (very low) to 5 (extreme)   **Total Score** _____

Activity - E.g. walking, weight exercise, classes   **Duration**

Type:

_____   _____

_____   _____

_____   _____

How do you feel overall?	Great | Good | Up & Down | Low	How did you sleep?	Great | Good | Poor | Hrs: ___

Diet - What did you eat today?

Did you have any of these phytoestrogenic foods today?

O Soy beans – edamame, tofu

O Peas and beans

O Lentils

O Seeds – flaxseed, sesame

O Fruits – banana, apple, orange

O Wholegrain and wheat bran

O Vegetables – cauliflower, broccoli, carrots, cabbage

O Berries and currants

O Other

See Page 17 for More Details

Total water intake (aim for 8 large glasses):

O   O   O   O   O   O   O   O

If you could summarise today in 3 words, what would they be?

1.

2.

3.

Thrive
Day 68

Date: ....

Reference the List on Page 39

Symptoms - Fill in the symptoms you are experiencing.

Symptoms:	Comments	Score

Score symptoms from 0 (very low) to 5 (extreme)   **Total Score** _____

Activity - E.g. walking, weight exercise, classes   **Duration**

Type:

How do you feel overall? Great | Good | Up & Down | Low

How did you sleep? Great | Good | Poor | Hrs: ____

Diet - What did you eat today?

Did you have any of these phytoestrogenic foods today?

O Soy beans – edamame, tofu

O Peas and beans

O Lentils

O Seeds – flaxseed, sesame

O Fruits – banana, apple, orange

O Wholegrain and wheat bran

O Vegetables – cauliflower, broccoli, carrots, cabbage

O Berries and currants

O Other

Total water intake (aim for 8 large glasses):

O   O   O   O   O   O   O   O

See Page 17 for More Details

If you could summarise today in 3 words, what would they be?

1.

2.

3.

Day 69

Date: ....

Reference the List on Page 39

Symptoms - Fill in the symptoms you are experiencing.

Symptoms:	Comments	Score
_____	_____	_____
_____	_____	_____
_____	_____	_____
_____	_____	_____
_____	_____	_____
_____	_____	_____
_____	_____	_____

Score symptoms from 0 (very low) to 5 (extreme)   **Total Score** _____

Activity - E.g. walking, weight exercise, classes   **Duration**

Type:

_____   _____

_____   _____

_____   _____

How do you feel overall? Great | Good | Up & Down | Low

How did you sleep? Great | Good | Poor | Hrs: ____

Diet - What did you eat today?

Did you have any of these phytoestrogenic foods today?

O Soy beans – edamame, tofu

O Peas and beans

O Lentils

O Seeds – flaxseed, sesame

O Fruits – banana, apple, orange

O Wholegrain and wheat bran

O Vegetables – cauliflower, broccoli, carrots, cabbage

O Berries and currants

O Other

See Page 17 for More Details

Total water intake (aim for 8 large glasses):

O   O   O   O   O   O   O   O

If you could summarise today in 3 words, what would they be?

1.

2.

3.

Thrive
Day 70

Date: ....

Reference the List on Page 39

Symptoms - Fill in the symptoms you are experiencing.

Symptoms:	Comments	Score
_____	_____	_____
_____	_____	_____
_____	_____	_____
_____	_____	_____
_____	_____	_____
_____	_____	_____
_____	_____	_____
_____	_____	_____

Score symptoms from 0 (very low) to 5 (extreme)   **Total Score** _____

Activity - E.g. walking, weight exercise, classes   **Duration**

Type:

_____   _____

_____   _____

_____   _____

How do you feel overall? Great | Good | Up & Down | Low

How did you sleep? Great | Good | Poor | Hrs: ___

Diet - What did you eat today?

Did you have any of these phytoestrogenic foods today?

O Soy beans – edamame, tofu

O Peas and beans

O Lentils

O Seeds – flaxseed, sesame

O Fruits – banana, apple, orange

O Wholegrain and wheat bran

O Vegetables – cauliflower, broccoli, carrots, cabbage

O Berries and currants

O Other

See Page 17 for More Details

Total water intake (aim for 8 large glasses):

O   O   O   O   O   O   O   O

If you could summarise today in 3 words, what would they be?

1.

2.

3.

" Life isn't about waiting for the storm to pass... It's about learning how to **dance in the rain**. "

Vivian Greene

The *Anger or Regret* Exercise

Do you have lingering resentments or regrets?
Do they trap you in the past and stop your progress?

Write a letter to the person who generates these
feelings (you do not have to send it) or write to your
younger self and offer advice and/or forgiveness.

Dear...

Thrive
Day 71

Date: ....

Reference the List on Page 39

Symptoms - Fill in the symptoms you are experiencing.

Symptoms:	Comments	Score
_____	_____	_____
_____	_____	_____
_____	_____	_____
_____	_____	_____
_____	_____	_____
_____	_____	_____
_____	_____	_____

Score symptoms from 0 (very low) to 5 (extreme)   **Total Score** _____

Activity - E.g. walking, weight exercise, classes   **Duration**

Type:

_____   _____

_____   _____

_____   _____

How do you feel overall? Great | Good | Up & Down | Low

How did you sleep? Great | Good | Poor | Hrs: ____

Diet - What did you eat today?

Did you have any of these phytoestrogenic foods today?

O Soy beans – edamame, tofu

O Peas and beans

O Lentils

O Seeds – flaxseed, sesame

O Fruits – banana, apple, orange

O Wholegrain and wheat bran

O Vegetables – cauliflower, broccoli, carrots, cabbage

O Berries and currants

O Other

Total water intake (aim for 8 large glasses):

O   O   O   O   O   O   O   O

See Page 17 for More Details

If you could summarise today in 3 words, what would they be?

1.   **2.**   **3.**

Thrive
Day 72

Date: ....

Reference the List on Page 39

Symptoms - Fill in the symptoms you are experiencing.

Symptoms:	Comments	Score
_____	_____	_____
_____	_____	_____
_____	_____	_____
_____	_____	_____
_____	_____	_____
_____	_____	_____
_____	_____	_____

Score symptoms from 0 (very low) to 5 (extreme)   **Total Score** _____

Activity - E.g. walking, weight exercise, classes   **Duration**

Type:

_____   _____

_____   _____

_____   _____

| How do you feel overall? | Great \| Good \| Up & Down \| Low | How did you sleep? | Great \| Good \| Poor \| Hrs: ___ |

Diet - What did you eat today?

Did you have any of these phytoestrogenic foods today?

O Soy beans – edamame, tofu

O Peas and beans

O Lentils

O Seeds – flaxseed, sesame

O Fruits – banana, apple, orange

O Wholegrain and wheat bran

O Vegetables – cauliflower, broccoli, carrots, cabbage

O Berries and currants

O Other

Total water intake (aim for 8 large glasses):

O   O   O   O   O   O   O   O

See Page 17 for More Details

If you could summarise today in 3 words, what would they be?

1.

2.

3.

Thrive
Day 73

Date: ....

Reference the List on Page 39

Symptoms - Fill in the symptoms you are experiencing.		
Symptoms:	Comments	Score
_____	_____	_____
_____	_____	_____
_____	_____	_____
_____	_____	_____
_____	_____	_____
_____	_____	_____
_____	_____	_____

Score symptoms from 0 (very low) to 5 (extreme)   **Total Score** _____

Activity - E.g. walking, weight exercise, classes	**Duration**
Type:	
_____	_____
_____	_____
_____	_____

| How do you feel overall? | Great \| Good \| Up & Down \| Low | How did you sleep? | Great \| Good \| Poor \| Hrs: ___ |

Diet - What did you eat today?

Did you have any of these phytoestrogenic foods today?

O Soy beans – edamame, tofu

O Peas and beans

O Lentils

O Seeds – flaxseed, sesame

O Fruits – banana, apple, orange

O Wholegrain and wheat bran

O Vegetables – cauliflower, broccoli, carrots, cabbage

O Berries and currants

O Other

Total water intake (aim for 8 large glasses):

O   O   O   O   O   O   O   O

See Page 17 for More Details

If you could summarise today in 3 words, what would they be?

1.

2.

3.

Thrive
Day 74

Date: ....

Reference the List on Page 39

Symptoms - Fill in the symptoms you are experiencing.

Symptoms:	Comments	Score
_____	_____	_____
_____	_____	_____
_____	_____	_____
_____	_____	_____
_____	_____	_____
_____	_____	_____
_____	_____	_____

Score symptoms from 0 (very low) to 5 (extreme)   **Total Score** _____

Activity - E.g. walking, weight exercise, classes   **Duration**

Type:
_____   _____

_____   _____

_____   _____

| How do you feel overall? | Great | Good | Up & Down | Low | How did you sleep? | Great | Good | Poor | Hrs: ___ |

Diet - What did you eat today?

Did you have any of these phytoestrogenic foods today?

O Soy beans – edamame, tofu

O Peas and beans

O Lentils

O Seeds – flaxseed, sesame

O Fruits – banana, apple, orange

O Wholegrain and wheat bran

O Vegetables – cauliflower, broccoli, carrots, cabbage

O Berries and currants

O Other

See Page 17 for More Details

Total water intake (aim for 8 large glasses):

O   O   O   O   O   O   O   O

If you could summarise today in 3 words, what would they be?

1.

2.

3.

Thrive
Day 75

Date: ....

Reference the List on Page 39

Symptoms - Fill in the symptoms you are experiencing.		
Symptoms:	Comments	Score
_____	_____	_____
_____	_____	_____
_____	_____	_____
_____	_____	_____
_____	_____	_____
_____	_____	_____
_____	_____	_____
_____	_____	_____

Score symptoms from 0 (very low) to 5 (extreme)   **Total Score** _____

Activity - E.g. walking, weight exercise, classes	Duration
Type:	
_____	_____
_____	_____
_____	_____

| How do you feel overall? | Great \| Good \| Up & Down \| Low | How did you sleep? | Great \| Good \| Poor \| Hrs: ___ |

Diet - What did you eat today?

Did you have any of these phytoestrogenic foods today?

O Soy beans – edamame, tofu

O Peas and beans

O Lentils

O Seeds – flaxseed, sesame

O Fruits – banana, apple, orange

O Wholegrain and wheat bran

O Vegetables – cauliflower, broccoli, carrots, cabbage

O Berries and currants

O Other

Total water intake (aim for 8 large glasses):

O   O   O   O   O   O   O   O

See Page 17 for More Details

If you could summarise today in 3 words, what would they be?

1.   **2.**   **3.**

Thrive
Day 76

Date: ....

Reference the List on Page 39

Symptoms - Fill in the symptoms you are experiencing.

Symptoms: Comments   Score

_____   _____   _____

_____   _____   _____

_____   _____   _____

_____   _____   _____

_____   _____   _____

_____   _____   _____

_____   _____   _____

Score symptoms from 0 (very low) to 5 (extreme)   **Total Score** _____

Activity - E.g. walking, weight exercise, classes   **Duration**

Type:

_____   _____

_____   _____

_____   _____

How do you feel overall? Great | Good | Up & Down | Low

How did you sleep? Great | Good | Poor | Hrs: ___

Diet - What did you eat today?

Did you have any of these phytoestrogenic foods today?

O Soy beans – edamame, tofu

O Peas and beans

O Lentils

O Seeds – flaxseed, sesame

O Fruits – banana, apple, orange

O Wholegrain and wheat bran

O Vegetables – cauliflower, broccoli, carrots, cabbage

O Berries and currants

O Other

Total water intake (aim for 8 large glasses):

O   O   O   O   O   O   O   O

See Page 17 for More Details

If you could summarise today in 3 words, what would they be?

1.

2.

3.

Thrive
Day 77

Date: ....

↙ Reference the List on Page 39

Symptoms - Fill in the symptoms you are experiencing.

Symptoms:	Comments	Score
_____	_____	_____
_____	_____	_____
_____	_____	_____
_____	_____	_____
_____	_____	_____
_____	_____	_____
_____	_____	_____

Score symptoms from 0 (very low) to 5 (extreme)   **Total Score** _____

Activity - E.g. walking, weight exercise, classes   **Duration**

Type:
_____   _____

_____   _____

_____   _____

| How do you feel overall? | Great \| Good \| Up & Down \| Low | How did you sleep? | Great \| Good \| Poor \| Hrs: ____ |

Diet - What did you eat today?

Did you have any of these phytoestrogenic foods today?

O Soy beans – edamame, tofu

O Peas and beans

O Lentils

O Seeds – flaxseed, sesame

O Fruits – banana, apple, orange

O Wholegrain and wheat bran

O Vegetables – cauliflower, broccoli, carrots, cabbage

O Berries and currants

O Other

See Page 17 for More Details

Total water intake (aim for 8 large glasses):

O   O   O   O   O   O   O   O

If you could summarise today in 3 words, what would they be?

1.

2.

3.

Cheryl Thallon

66 Nature creates the menopause but thankfully **nature's remedies** are there to support us. 99

The *Morning Rituals* Exercise

Starting your day with positivity. Write down your morning rituals. Your non-negotiable time for yourself.
This could include 30 minutes exercise, a large glass of a water, 10 minutes of meditation, acts of service (such as washing up or getting the kitchen ready for the day), playing with your dog, or five minutes silence in the garden.

Write down the ways you will 'own' your morning.

I will...

I will...

I will...

I will...

I will...

I will...

I will...

I will...

I will...

I will...

This exercise can be repeated as often as is needed.

Thrive
Day 78

Date: ....

Reference the List on Page 39

Symptoms - Fill in the symptoms you are experiencing.

Symptoms:	Comments	Score
_____	_____	_____
_____	_____	_____
_____	_____	_____
_____	_____	_____
_____	_____	_____
_____	_____	_____
_____	_____	_____
_____	_____	_____

Score symptoms from 0 (very low) to 5 (extreme)   **Total Score** _____

Activity - E.g. walking, weight exercise, classes   **Duration**

Type:

_____   _____

_____   _____

_____   _____

| How do you feel overall? | Great | Good | Up & Down | Low | How did you sleep? | Great | Good | Poor | Hrs: ___ |

Diet - What did you eat today?

Did you have any of these phytoestrogenic foods today?

O Soy beans – edamame, tofu

O Peas and beans

O Lentils

O Seeds – flaxseed, sesame

O Fruits – banana, apple, orange

O Wholegrain and wheat bran

O Vegetables – cauliflower, broccoli, carrots, cabbage

O Berries and currants

O Other

Total water intake (aim for 8 large glasses):

O   O   O   O   O   O   O   O

See Page 17 for More Details

If you could summarise today in 3 words, what would they be?

1.

2.

3.

Thrive
Day 79

Date: ....

Reference the List on Page 39

Symptoms - Fill in the symptoms you are experiencing.

Symptoms:	Comments	Score
_____	_____	_____
_____	_____	_____
_____	_____	_____
_____	_____	_____
_____	_____	_____
_____	_____	_____
_____	_____	_____
_____	_____	_____

Score symptoms from 0 (very low) to 5 (extreme)   **Total Score** _____

Activity - E.g. walking, weight exercise, classes   **Duration**

Type:

_____ _____

_____ _____

_____ _____

How do you feel overall? Great | Good | Up & Down | Low

How did you sleep? Great | Good | Poor | Hrs: ____

Diet - What did you eat today?

Did you have any of these phytoestrogenic foods today?

O Soy beans – edamame, tofu

O Peas and beans

O Lentils

O Seeds – flaxseed, sesame

O Fruits – banana, apple, orange

O Wholegrain and wheat bran

O Vegetables – cauliflower, broccoli, carrots, cabbage

O Berries and currants

O Other

See Page 17 for More Details

Total water intake (aim for 8 large glasses):

O   O   O   O   O   O   O   O

If you could summarise today in 3 words, what would they be?

1.

2.

3.

Thrive
Day 80

Date: ....

Reference the List on Page 39

Symptoms - Fill in the symptoms you are experiencing.

Symptoms:	Comments	Score
_____	_____	_____
_____	_____	_____
_____	_____	_____
_____	_____	_____
_____	_____	_____
_____	_____	_____
_____	_____	_____

Score symptoms from 0 (very low) to 5 (extreme)   **Total Score** _____

Activity - E.g. walking, weight exercise, classes | Duration

Type:

| How do you feel overall? | Great \| Good \| Up & Down \| Low | How did you sleep? | Great \| Good \| Poor \| Hrs: ___ |

Diet - What did you eat today?

Did you have any of these phytoestrogenic foods today?

O Soy beans – edamame, tofu

O Peas and beans

O Lentils

O Seeds – flaxseed, sesame

O Fruits – banana, apple, orange

O Wholegrain and wheat bran

O Vegetables – cauliflower, broccoli, carrots, cabbage

O Berries and currants

O Other

See Page 17 for More Details

Total water intake (aim for 8 large glasses):

O   O   O   O   O   O   O   O

If you could summarise today in 3 words, what would they be?

1.

2.

3.

Thrive
Day 81

Date: ....

Reference the List on Page 39

Symptoms - Fill in the symptoms you are experiencing.

Symptoms:	Comments	Score
_____	_____	_____
_____	_____	_____
_____	_____	_____
_____	_____	_____
_____	_____	_____
_____	_____	_____
_____	_____	_____
_____	_____	_____

Score symptoms from 0 (very low) to 5 (extreme)   **Total Score** _____

Activity - E.g. walking, weight exercise, classes   **Duration**

Type:

_____   _____

_____   _____

_____   _____

| How do you feel overall? | Great | Good | Up & Down | Low | How did you sleep? | Great | Good | Poor | Hrs: ____ |

Diet - What did you eat today?

Did you have any of these phytoestrogenic foods today?

O Soy beans – edamame, tofu

O Peas and beans

O Lentils

O Seeds – flaxseed, sesame

O Fruits – banana, apple, orange

O Wholegrain and wheat bran

O Vegetables – cauliflower, broccoli, carrots, cabbage

O Berries and currants

O Other

See Page 17 for More Details

Total water intake (aim for 8 large glasses):

O   O   O   O   O   O   O   O

If you could summarise today in 3 words, what would they be?

1.   **2.**   **3.**

Thrive
Day 82

Date: ....

Reference the List on Page 39

Symptoms - Fill in the symptoms you are experiencing.		
Symptoms:	Comments	Score
_____	_____	_____
_____	_____	_____
_____	_____	_____
_____	_____	_____
_____	_____	_____
_____	_____	_____
_____	_____	_____

Score symptoms from 0 (very low) to 5 (extreme) **Total Score** _____

Activity - E.g. walking, weight exercise, classes	**Duration**
Type:	
_____	_____
_____	_____
_____	_____

| How do you feel overall? | Great \| Good \| Up & Down \| Low | How did you sleep? | Great \| Good \| Poor \| Hrs: ___ |

Diet - What did you eat today?

Did you have any of these phytoestrogenic foods today?

O Soy beans – edamame, tofu

O Peas and beans

O Lentils

O Seeds – flaxseed, sesame

O Fruits – banana, apple, orange

O Wholegrain and wheat bran

O Vegetables – cauliflower, broccoli, carrots, cabbage

O Berries and currants

O Other

See Page 17 for More Details

Total water intake (aim for 8 large glasses):

O   O   O   O   O   O   O   O

If you could summarise today in 3 words, what would they be?

1.   **2.**   **3.**

Thrive
Day 83

Date: ....

Reference the List on Page 39

Symptoms - Fill in the symptoms you are experiencing.

Symptoms:	Comments	Score

Score symptoms from 0 (very low) to 5 (extreme) **Total Score** _____

Activity - E.g. walking, weight exercise, classes   **Duration**

Type:

| How do you feel overall? | Great \| Good \| Up & Down \| Low | How did you sleep? | Great \| Good \| Poor \| Hrs: ____ |

Diet - What did you eat today?

Did you have any of these phytoestrogenic foods today?

O Soy beans – edamame, tofu

O Peas and beans

O Lentils

O Seeds – flaxseed, sesame

O Fruits – banana, apple, orange

O Wholegrain and wheat bran

O Vegetables – cauliflower, broccoli, carrots, cabbage

O Berries and currants

O Other

See Page 17 for More Details

Total water intake (aim for 8 large glasses):

O   O   O   O   O   O   O   O

If you could summarise today in 3 words, what would they be?

1.

2.

3.

Thrive
Day 84

Date: ....

Reference the List on Page 39

Symptoms - Fill in the symptoms you are experiencing.

Symptoms:	Comments	Score
_____	_____	____
_____	_____	____
_____	_____	____
_____	_____	____
_____	_____	____
_____	_____	____
_____	_____	____

Score symptoms from 0 (very low) to 5 (extreme)   **Total Score** _____

Activity - E.g. walking, weight exercise, classes   **Duration**

Type:

_____   _____

_____   _____

_____   _____

| How do you feel overall? | Great | Good | Up & Down | Low | How did you sleep? | Great | Good | Poor | Hrs: ___ |

Diet - What did you eat today?

Did you have any of these phytoestrogenic foods today?

O Soy beans – edamame, tofu

O Peas and beans

O Lentils

O Seeds – flaxseed, sesame

O Fruits – banana, apple, orange

O Wholegrain and wheat bran

O Vegetables – cauliflower, broccoli, carrots, cabbage

O Berries and currants

O Other

See Page 17 for More Details

Total water intake (aim for 8 large glasses):

O   O   O   O   O   O   O   O

If you could summarise today in 3 words, what would they be?

1.

2.

3.

> **" When one door of happiness closes, another opens** but often we look so long at the closed door that we do not see the one which has been opened for us. **"**

Helen Keller

The *Proximity* Exercise

If you had an imaginary dinner party with 8 guests and you could invite anyone in the world, dead or alive, who would you choose?

In real life, who are the people you actually spend most time with? Manage and protect your energy by spending time with those who excite and inspire you.

Guest #1...

Guest #2...

Guest #3...

Guest #4...

Guest #5...

Guest #6...

Guest #7...

Guest #8...

This exercise can be repeated as often as is needed.

Thrive
Day 85

Date: ....

Reference the List on Page 39

Symptoms - Fill in the symptoms you are experiencing.		
Symptoms:	Comments	Score
_____	_____	_____
_____	_____	_____
_____	_____	_____
_____	_____	_____
_____	_____	_____
_____	_____	_____
_____	_____	_____
_____	_____	_____
Score symptoms from 0 (very low) to 5 (extreme)		**Total Score** _____

Activity - E.g. walking, weight exercise, classes	**Duration**
Type:	
_____	_____
_____	_____
_____	_____

| How do you feel overall? | Great | Good | Up & Down | Low | How did you sleep? | Great | Good | Poor | Hrs: ___ |

Diet - What did you eat today?

Did you have any of these phytoestrogenic foods today?

O Soy beans – edamame, tofu

O Peas and beans

O Lentils

O Seeds – flaxseed, sesame

O Fruits – banana, apple, orange

O Wholegrain and wheat bran

O Vegetables – cauliflower, broccoli, carrots, cabbage

O Berries and currants

O Other

See Page 17 for More Details

Total water intake (aim for 8 large glasses):

O   O   O   O   O   O   O   O

If you could summarise today in 3 words, what would they be?

1.   **2.**   **3.**

Thrive
Day 86

Date: ....

Reference the List on Page 39

Symptoms - Fill in the symptoms you are experiencing.		
Symptoms:	**Comments**	**Score**
_____	_____	_____
_____	_____	_____
_____	_____	_____
_____	_____	_____
_____	_____	_____
_____	_____	_____
_____	_____	_____

Score symptoms from 0 (very low) to 5 (extreme)   **Total Score** _____

Activity - E.g. walking, weight exercise, classes	Duration
Type:	
_____	_____
_____	_____
_____	_____

How do you feel overall? Great | Good | Up & Down | Low

How did you sleep? Great | Good | Poor | Hrs: ___

Diet - What did you eat today?

Did you have any of these phytoestrogenic foods today?

O Soy beans – edamame, tofu

O Peas and beans

O Lentils

O Seeds – flaxseed, sesame

O Fruits – banana, apple, orange

O Wholegrain and wheat bran

O Vegetables – cauliflower, broccoli, carrots, cabbage

O Berries and currants

O Other

See Page 17 for More Details

Total water intake (aim for 8 large glasses):

O   O   O   O   O   O   O   O

If you could summarise today in 3 words, what would they be?

1.

2.

3.

Thrive
Day 87

Date: ....

Reference the List on Page 39

Symptoms - Fill in the symptoms you are experiencing.

Symptoms:	Comments	Score
_____	_____	_____
_____	_____	_____
_____	_____	_____
_____	_____	_____
_____	_____	_____
_____	_____	_____
_____	_____	_____
_____	_____	_____

Score symptoms from 0 (very low) to 5 (extreme)   **Total Score** _____

Activity - E.g. walking, weight exercise, classes   **Duration**

Type:

_____   _____

_____   _____

_____   _____

| How do you feel overall? | Great | Good | Up & Down | Low | | How did you sleep? | Great | Good | Poor | Hrs: ___ |

Diet - What did you eat today?

Did you have any of these phytoestrogenic foods today?

O Soy beans – edamame, tofu

O Peas and beans

O Lentils

O Seeds – flaxseed, sesame

O Fruits – banana, apple, orange

O Wholegrain and wheat bran

O Vegetables – cauliflower, broccoli, carrots, cabbage

O Berries and currants

O Other

Total water intake (aim for 8 large glasses):

O   O   O   O   O   O   O   O

See Page 17 for More Details

If you could summarise today in 3 words, what would they be?

1.

2.

3.

Thrive
Day 88

Date: ....

Reference the List on Page 39

Symptoms - Fill in the symptoms you are experiencing.		
Symptoms:	Comments	Score
_____	_____	_____
_____	_____	_____
_____	_____	_____
_____	_____	_____
_____	_____	_____
_____	_____	_____
_____	_____	_____

Score symptoms from 0 (very low) to 5 (extreme)   **Total Score** _____

Activity - E.g. walking, weight exercise, classes	Duration
Type:	
_____	_____
_____	_____
_____	_____

How do you feel overall?   Great | Good | Up & Down | Low

How did you sleep?   Great | Good | Poor | Hrs: ____

Diet - What did you eat today?

Did you have any of these phytoestrogenic foods today?

O Soy beans – edamame, tofu

O Peas and beans

O Lentils

O Seeds – flaxseed, sesame

O Fruits – banana, apple, orange

O Wholegrain and wheat bran

O Vegetables – cauliflower, broccoli, carrots, cabbage

O Berries and currants

O Other

See Page 17 for More Details

Total water intake (aim for 8 large glasses):

O   O   O   O   O   O   O   O

If you could summarise today in 3 words, what would they be?

1.

2.

3.

Thrive
Day 89

Date: ....

Reference the List on Page 39

Symptoms - Fill in the symptoms you are experiencing.

Symptoms:	Comments	Score
_____	_____	_____
_____	_____	_____
_____	_____	_____
_____	_____	_____
_____	_____	_____
_____	_____	_____
_____	_____	_____

Score symptoms from 0 (very low) to 5 (extreme)   **Total Score** _____

Activity - E.g. walking, weight exercise, classes   **Duration**

Type:

| How do you feel overall? | Great | Good | Up & Down | Low | How did you sleep? | Great | Good | Poor | Hrs: ___ |

Diet - What did you eat today?

Did you have any of these phytoestrogenic foods today?

O Soy beans – edamame, tofu

O Peas and beans

O Lentils

O Seeds – flaxseed, sesame

O Fruits – banana, apple, orange

O Wholegrain and wheat bran

O Vegetables – cauliflower, broccoli, carrots, cabbage

O Berries and currants

O Other

Total water intake (aim for 8 large glasses):

O   O   O   O   O   O   O   O

See Page 17 for More Details

If you could summarise today in 3 words, what would they be?

1.

2.

3.

Thrive
Day 90

Date: ....

Reference the List on Page 39

Symptoms - Fill in the symptoms you are experiencing.		
Symptoms:	Comments	Score
_____	_____	_____
_____	_____	_____
_____	_____	_____
_____	_____	_____
_____	_____	_____
_____	_____	_____
_____	_____	_____

Score symptoms from 0 (very low) to 5 (extreme)　**Total Score** _____

Activity - E.g. walking, weight exercise, classes	Duration
Type:	
_____	_____
_____	_____
_____	_____

| How do you feel overall? | Great | Good | Up & Down | Low | How did you sleep? | Great | Good | Poor | Hrs: ___ |

Diet - What did you eat today?

Did you have any of these phytoestrogenic foods today?

O Soy beans – edamame, tofu

O Peas and beans

O Lentils

O Seeds – flaxseed, sesame

O Fruits – banana, apple, orange

O Wholegrain and wheat bran

O Vegetables – cauliflower, broccoli, carrots, cabbage

O Berries and currants

O Other

See Page 17 for More Details

Total water intake (aim for 8 large glasses):

O   O   O   O   O   O   O   O

If you could summarise today in 3 words, what would they be?

1.

2.

3.

Day 91

Three months are now complete and you should be feeling the benefits of your personalised program. Why not help others and share your story on social media #TheMenopauseJournal

Date: ....

Reference the List on Page 39

Symptoms - Fill in the symptoms you are experiencing.

Symptoms:	Comments	Score
_____	_____	_____
_____	_____	_____
_____	_____	_____
_____	_____	_____
_____	_____	_____
_____	_____	_____
_____	_____	_____

Score symptoms from 0 (very low) to 5 (extreme)   **Total Score** _____

Activity - E.g. walking, weight exercise, classes   **Duration**

Type:

_____   _____

_____   _____

_____   _____

| How do you feel overall? | Great | Good | Up & Down | Low | How did you sleep? | Great | Good | Poor | Hrs: ___ |

Diet - What did you eat today?

Did you have any of these phytoestrogenic foods today?

O Soy beans – edamame, tofu

O Peas and beans

O Lentils

O Seeds – flaxseed, sesame

O Fruits – banana, apple, orange

O Wholegrain and wheat bran

O Vegetables – cauliflower, broccoli, carrots, cabbage

O Berries and currants

O Other

See Page 17 for More Details

Total water intake (aim for 8 large glasses):

O   O   O   O   O   O   O   O

If you could summarise today in 3 words, what would they be?

1.

2.

3.

Maya Angelou

" My mission in life is not merely to survive, but to thrive; and to **do so with some passion** to reinvent yourself after years of focusing on the needs of everyone else. It's your opportunity to get clear about what matters to you and then to pursue that with all of your energy, time and talent. "

The *Longevity* Exercise

This task will help focus your mind on what is really important to you, and how you truly want to spend your time.

On this chart, draw a horizontal red line from your age on the left all the way to the right.
Colour the space below the line.

How long do you spend each night sleeping?
Block out those hours with a vertical line.

How long do you spend each day working and completing chores such as washing, cleaning, tidying, ironing? Block out those hours with a vertical line.

How long do you spend each day watching tv?
Block out those hours with a vertical line.

The box in the top right hand corner is how much productive time you have left (if you live to 100). How do you want to spend it?

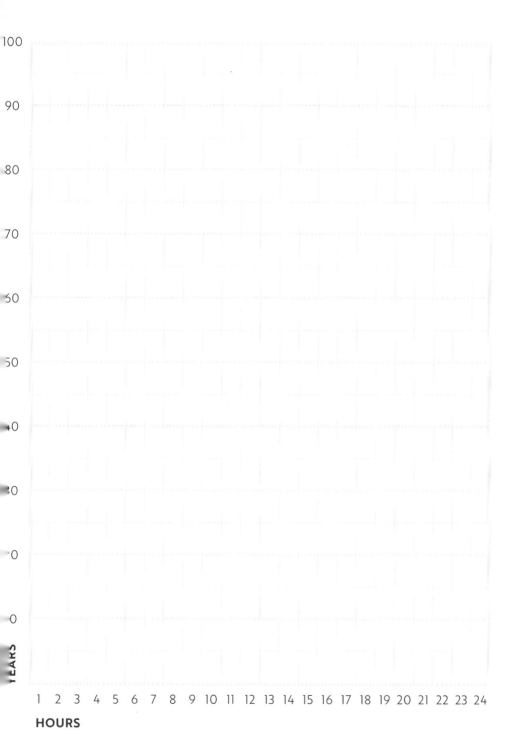

HOURS

YEARS

This exercise can be repeated as often as is needed.

You've got this!

Now the 90 days are complete, I hope you are feeling empowered to manage your menopause, your way. This is just the beginning. The new habits you've adopted along with the right diet and lifestyle choices will help fuel your body to a greater level of nutrient density that will make you healthier, happier and better able to live the life you want – through the menopause and beyond.

This is an ideal time to look back and see what you have achieved. At the start of the 3 months, you wrote down some goals. Take a moment now to review where you are and what more you want to achieve. Write down what actions you need to take to grow further and what promises are you making to your future self.

Keep hold of this journal to remind you of the success you've had and the positive outcomes you've experienced. Remember you are in control and you now have a daily routine to help embrace the changes you are experiencing. Be kind to yourself and don't forget you are not alone, there are lots of options available to support you. You've got this!

Wishing you abundant health and happiness...

Aimée Benbow

BSc (Hons) MSc ANutr

My journey so far...

How I feel now:

_____

_____

_____

_____

_____

_____

What I'm really proud of:

_____

_____

_____

_____

_____

_____

_____

_____

_____

New strengths I've discovered:

_____

_____

_____

_____

_____

_____

_____

_____

What I've achieved in the last 3 months:

_____

_____

_____

_____

_____

_____

_____

_____

_____

My favourite healthy foods:

_____

_____

_____

_____

_____

_____

_____

_____

What I'm grateful for:

_____

_____

_____

_____

_____

_____

5 ways I am kind to myself:

_____

_____

_____

_____

_____

_____

_____

New things I want to try:

_____

_____

_____

_____

_____

_____

_____

What I want to improve:

_____

_____

_____

_____

_____

_____

Actions I need to take:

_____

_____

_____

_____

_____

_____

Promises to myself in the next ___ months:

_____

_____

_____

_____

_____

Food supplement glossary

Angelica archangelica - Commonly known as garden angelica or wild celery, angelica is native to northern Scandinavian countries. This herb has undergone research with positive outcomes for its effects relaxing the bladder wall and therefore allowing the bladder to hold more total urine, reducing the likelihood of incontinence [66].

Ashwagandha - One of the most highly prized plants for rejuvenating and strengthening the mind and body, ashwagandha (*Withania somnifera*) has been used as a nutritional tonic for thousands of years. Ashwagandha is especially valued as a nerve tonic, to reduce stress, and as a memory enhancer, and modern research supports this traditional use [67]. Evidence suggests it can assist in alleviating some of the temperature dysregulating symptoms particularly during the perimenopause stage. A study on women supplementing with 300mg of ashwagandha daily found significant improvements in hot flushes as well as general quality of life scores during this time [68].

B Complex – As well as assisting the body with energy production, B vitamins, specifically B6, B12 and folic acid may be of particular importance for those taking HRT as evidence suggests that the absorption of these essential nutrients, along with magnesium, can be impacted by medication containing oestrogens [69].

Biotin - Generally classified as a B vitamin, biotin is important for heathy hair, skin and nails. It is found in food sources such as nuts, eggs, root vegetables and can be taken as a food supplement. Thinning hair is a common menopausal symptom, due to the drop in oestrogen which plays a regulatory role in hair growth and hair loss. Therefore, obtaining additional biotin in the diet can be beneficial.

Borage and Evening primrose oil – The omega-6 fatty acid found in borage and evening primrose oil has demonstrated strong benefits in regulating hormone balance. This in turn can lessen the severity of menopausal symptoms, in particular hot flushes and night sweats [70]. Additionally, omega oils play an important role in skin health and can assist with skin and tissue structure and flexibility.

Calcium - Menopause is associated with reduced bone mass, therefore, supplementing with calcium is essential to maintain the bones and prevent osteoporosis. Calcium alongside vitamin D3 and vitamin K2 work together to support bone density.

Cranberry and Mannose – These can work well together to help those suffering with urinary tract infections (UTIs). Evidence suggests that UTIs can become more common during the menopause, and both cranberry extract [71] (without the natural sugars present in this fruit), plus mannose [72] can assist by preventing bacteria adhering to the urinary walls, therefore treating the infection.

Curcumin – This is the active compound in turmeric which gives this spice its infamous orange colour, is also well known to possess anti-inflammatory properties. Supplementation with curcumin has demonstrated benefits comparable to NSAIDs, such as ibuprofen, in those suffering with inflamed joint conditions [73]. Additionally, a trial found menopausal women who supplemented with curcumin alongside vitamin E, experienced a significant reduction in the frequency of hot flushes [74].

Fish oil – Fish oil supplements sourced from freshwater lakes, and seed oils such as flaxseed and perilla seed oil are naturally rich in omega-3, which has proven benefits for numerous areas of health including cardiovascular [75], skin, joint pain [76] and inflammation [77].

Holy basil - Also known as 'Tulsi', holy basil has featured in Ayurvedic medicine for centuries. Daily consumption is believed to prevent disease, promote general health, wellbeing and longevity, and assist in dealing with the stresses of daily life. Studies have noted its benefits for cases of generalised anxiety [78].

Hops – Often better known for brewing beer, the hops flower (*Hummus lupulus strobile*) is a rich source of the flavonoid and phytoestrogen, 8 prenylnaringenin, (8-PN). Hops extract standardised to 8-PN has been well studied for its benefits in relieving common menopause symptoms. In one study lasting 16 weeks, supplementation with hops extract significantly reduced a number of menopause associated discomforts including night sweats and hot flushes [79].

Iodine – This is an essential nutrient for the function of the thyroid gland. The thyroid gland, located in the neck, is responsible for numerous bodily functions including metabolism. The speed of metabolism has been observed to decline in women going through the menopause, therefore ensuring you get sufficient intake of iodine in the diet either through seafood and fish sources, or a food supplement can ensure optimal function of the thyroid gland.

Lemon balm - This aromatic herb contains an active called 'rosmarinic acid' which has shown in clinical trials to demonstrate clear benefits regarding memory and cognitive performance during the menopause. Lemon balm can also assist with sleep issues associated with menopause [80].

Maca - Sometimes referred to as 'Peruvian Ginseng', maca (*Lepidium meyenii*) is a radish-like root vegetable native to Peru. It is an adaptogen which means it can help to increase the body's ability to deal with physical and mental stressors, including menopausal symptoms. Maca has also shown to act as a natural aphrodisiac and help improve energy levels and reduce the likelihood of fatigue. Therefore, maca may also be of benefit for those who experience reduced libido during this time [81].

Magnesium - This essential mineral is involved in a multitude of enzymatic reactions in the body and works synergistically with calcium to promote bone health. Supplementing with magnesium can also help relieve symptoms such as stress, anxiety, and insomnia. Magnesium and vitamin B6 in combination has been specifically reviewed for its benefits on pre-menstrual symptoms (PMS) and low mood [82].

Probiotics – These are friendly bacteria for the gut which can be useful for many areas of health. However, getting the right balance of friendly bacteria in the gut can be a useful method to alleviate some of the digestive complaints which accompany the menopause such as constipation, bloating and irritable bowel syndrome. It is recommended that probiotics are taken alongside prebiotics, unless there is known sensitivity to prebiotic ingredients.

Rhodiola - Also known as arctic root or golden root, is indigenous to the polar arctic regions of eastern Siberia. As a powerful adaptogen rhodiola, offers broad non-specific effects supporting overall body function particularly, adrenal stress. There is also some initial evidence that rhodiola can act as a selective oestrogen receptor modulator (SERM) potentially reducing some of the symptoms of menopause [83].

Saffron – This highly prized spice from the crocus flower, has long been used to improve mood and wellbeing. Clinical studies have shown that 30mg of saffron extract daily can reduce the symptoms of low mood and depression during menopause [84].

Sage and Red clover – Both of these herbals act as phytoestrogens, reducing vasomotor symptoms such as hot flushes and sweating. A study supplementing menopausal women experiencing hot flushes with sage for 8 weeks noted a 50% reduction in the intensity of hot flushes [85]. Similar outcomes have been reported across research looking at red clover [86].

Shatavari - This is a species of asparagus that is native to India and the Himalayas. It is considered both a general tonic and a female reproductive tonic and is naturally high in isoflavones. Evidence has shown that consumption of therapeutic levels of shatavari can relieve pathologies associated with menopause, such as osteoporosis, through its oestrogenic mechanisms. A trial on postmenopausal women whereby the treatment group consumed shatavari for 10 weeks found a significant reduction in bone loss and increase in bone formation was seen [87].

Vitamin C – Plays an important role in the body's own production of collagen. Collagen [88] is needed for tissue and skin structure, so by increasing your vitamin C intake you can improve collagen production, and hence the overall appearance of skin. This is of particular importance for those experiencing thinning skin and the visibility of fine lines and wrinkles.

Further resources and references

Find a menopause specialist
British Menopause Society
www.thebms.org.uk/find-a-menopause-specialist/

Find an independent health store
www.findahealthstore.com

National Association of Health Stores
www.nahs.co.uk

Find a qualified nutritional therapist
British Association for Nutrition and Lifestyle Medicine
www.bant.org.uk

More information about healthy eating
Healthy Does It
www.healthydoesit.org

The Foundations of Nutrition Book. Jenny Carson
www.viridian-nutrition.com/Shop/books/Foundations_of_Nutrition.aspx

Vitamins and supplements
Viridian Nutrition
www.viridian-nutrition.com

Fitness
Dawn French
www.twdfitness.co.uk

Psychological wellbeing
Improving Access to Psychological Therapies Services (NHS)
www.nhs.uk/service-search/mental-health/find-a-psychological-therapies-service/

1 Nhs.uk. 2022. Menopause. [online] Available at: <https://www.nhs.uk/conditions/menopause/> [Accessed 28 August 2022].

2 NICE. 2022. Women with symptoms of menopause should not suffer in silence. [online] Available at: <https://www.nice.org.uk/news/article/women-with-symptoms-of-menopause-should-not-suffer-insilence#:~:text=An%20estimated%201.5%20million%20women,severely%20affect%20a%20woman's%20life.> [Accessed 28 August 2022].

3 Joffe, H., Massler, A. and Sharkey, K., 2010. Evaluation and Management of Sleep Disturbance during the Menopause Transition. Seminars in Reproductive Medicine, 28(05), pp.404-421.

4 Rybaczyk, L., Bashaw, M., Pathak, D., Moody, S., Gilders, R. and Holzschu, D., 2005. An overlooked connection: serotonergic mediation of estrogen-related physiology and pathology. BMC Women's Health, 5(1).

5 Kołodyńska, G., Zalewski, M. and Rożek-Piechura, K., 2019. Urinary incontinence in postmenopausal women – causes, symptoms, treatment. Menopausal Review, 18(1), pp.46-50.

6 Thurston, R., 2013. Cognition and the menopausal transition. Menopause, 20(12), pp.1231-1232.

7 Sniekers, Y., Weinans, H., van Osch, G. and van Leeuwen, J., 2010. Oestrogen is important for maintenance of cartilage and subchondral bone in a murine model of knee osteoarthritis. Arthritis Research & Therapy, 12(5).

8 Kozakowski, J., Gietka-Czernel, M., Leszczyńska, D. and Majos, A., 2017. Obesity in menopause – our negligence or an unfortunate inevitability?. Menopausal Review, 2, pp.61-65.

9 Argilés, J., Campos, N., Lopez-Pedrosa, J., Rueda, R. and Rodriguez-Mañas, L., 2016. Skeletal Muscle Regulates Metabolism via Interorgan Crosstalk: Roles in Health and Disease. Journal of the American Medical Directors Association, 17(9), pp.789-796.

10 Carr, M., 2003. The Emergence of the Metabolic Syndrome with Menopause. The Journal of Clinical Endocrinology & Metabolism, 88(6), pp.2404-2411.

11 Mahajan A, Patni R, Gupta V. Menopause and Cardiovascular Disease. J Midlife Health. 2019 Apr-Jun;10(2):55-56. doi: 10.4103/0976-7800.261983. PMID: 31391752; PMCID: PMC6643715

12 Ji, M. and Yu, Q., 2015. Primary osteoporosis in postmenopausal women. Maturitas, 82(3), p.315.

13 Vinogradova, Y., Coupland, C. and Hippisley-Cox, J., 2019. Use of hormone replacement therapy and risk of venous thromboembolism: nested case-control studies using the QResearch and CPRD databases. BMJ, p.k4810.

14 The Lancet, 2019. Type and timing of menopausal hormone therapy and breast cancer risk: individual participant meta-analysis of the worldwide epidemiological evidence. 394(10204), pp.1159-1168.

15 Wells, G., Tugwell, P., Shea, B., Guyatt, G., Peterson, J., Zytaruk, N., Robinson, V., Henry, D., O'Connell, D. and Cranney, A., 2002. Meta-analyses of therapies for postmenopausal osteoporosis. V. Meta-analysis of the efficacy of hormone replacement therapy in treating and preventing osteoporosis in postmenopausal women. Endocrine reviews, 23(4), pp.529-539.

16 Taylor, J.E., Baig, M.S., Helmy, T. and Gersh, F.L., 2021. Controversies Regarding Postmenopausal Hormone Replacement Therapy for Primary Cardiovascular Disease Prevention in Women. Cardiology in Review, 29(6), pp.296-304.

17 Journal of Nurse-Midwifery, 1983. Clonidine for hot flashes Laufer L, Erlik Y, Meldrum D, Judd H. Effect of clonidine on hot flashes in postmenopausal women. Obstet Gynecol 60:583, 1982. 28(2), pp.40-41.

18 Shams, T., Firwana, B., Habib, F., Alshahrani, A., AlNouh, B., Murad, M. and Ferwana, M., 2013. SSRIs for Hot Flashes: A Systematic Review and Meta-Analysis of Randomized Trials. Journal of General Internal Medicine, 29(1), pp.204-213.

19 Golomb, B., Evans, M., Dimsdale, J. and White, H., 2012. Effects of Statins on Energy and Fatigue With Exertion: Results From a Randomized Controlled Trial. Archives of Internal Medicine, 172(15).

20 Serra-Majem, L., Roman, B. and Estruch, R., 2006. Scientific evidence of interventions using the Mediterranean diet: a systematic review. Nutrition reviews, 64(suppl_1), pp.S27-S47.

21 Flor-Alemany, M., Marín-Jiménez, N., Coll-Risco, I., Aranda, P. and Aparicio, V., 2020. Influence of dietary habits and Mediterranean diet adherence on menopausal symptoms. The FLAMENCO project. Menopause, 27(9), pp.1015-1021.

22 Sayón-Orea, C., Santiago, S., Cuervo, M., Martínez-González, M., Garcia, A. and Martínez, J., 2015. Adherence to Mediterranean dietary pattern and menopausal symptoms in relation to overweight/obesity in Spanish perimenopausal and postmenopausal women. Menopause, 22(7), pp.750-757.

23 Chen, M., Lin, C. and Liu, C., 2014. Efficacy of phytoestrogens for menopausal symptoms: a meta-analysis and systematic review. Climacteric, 18(2), pp.260-269.

24 Tanwar, A.K., Dhiman, N., Kumar, A. and Jaitak, V., 2021. Engagement of phytoestrogens in breast cancer suppression: Structural classification and mechanistic approach. European Journal of Medicinal Chemistry, 213, p.113037.

25 Speirs, V., Carder, P., Lane, S., Dodwell, D., Lansdown, M. and Hanby, A., 2004. Oestrogen receptor β: what it means for patients with breast cancer. The Lancet Oncology, 5(3), pp.174-181.

26 Prakash, D. and Gupta, C., 2011. Role of phytoestrogens as nutraceuticals in human health. Pharmacologyonline, 1, pp.510-523.

27 Desmawati, D. and Sulastri, D., 2019. A Phytoestrogens and Their Health Effect. Open Access Macedonian Journal of Medical Sciences, 7(3), pp.495-499.

28 Lock, M., 2002. Symptom reporting at menopause: a review of cross-cultural findings. British Menopause Society Journal, 8(4), pp.132-136.

29 Kolesnikova, L., Semenova, N., Madaeva, I., Suturina, L., Solodova, E., Grebenkina, L. and Darenskaya, M., 2015. Antioxidant status in peri- and postmenopausal women. Maturitas, 81(1), pp.83-87.

30 Abshirini, M., Siassi, F., Koohdani, F., Qorbani, M., Khosravi, S., Hedayati, M., Aslani, Z., Soleymani, M. and Sotoudeh, G., 2018. Dietary total antioxidant capacity is inversely related to menopausal symptoms: a cross-sectional study among Iranian postmenopausal women. Nutrition, 55-56, pp.161-167.

31 Benbrook, C.M., 2005. Elevating antioxidant levels in food through organic farming and food processing (pp. 1-20). Washington, DC: Organic Center.

32 Wall, R., Ross, R., Fitzgerald, G. and Stanton, C., 2010. Fatty acids from fish: the anti-inflammatory potential of long-chain omega-3 fatty acids. Nutrition Reviews, 68(5), pp.280-289.

33 Freeman, M., Hibbeln, J., Silver, M., Hirschberg, A., Wang, B., Yule, A., Petrillo, L., Pascuillo, E., Economou, N., Joffe, H. and Cohen, L., 2011. Omega-3 fatty acids for major depressive disorder associated with the menopausal transition. Menopause, 18(3), pp.279-284.

34 Goldberg, R.J. and Katz, J., 2007. A meta-analysis of the analgesic effects of omega-3 polyunsaturated fatty acid supplementation for inflammatory joint pain. Pain, 129(1-2), pp.210-223.

35 Alexander, D.D., Miller, P.E., Van Elswyk, M.E., Kuratko, C.N. and Bylsma, L.C., 2017, January. A meta-analysis of randomized controlled trials and prospective cohort studies of eicosapentaenoic and docosahexaenoic long-chain omega-3 fatty acids and coronary heart disease risk. In Mayo Clinic Proceedings (Vol. 92, No. 1, pp. 15-29). Elsevier.

36 Banerjee, S., Gangopadhyay, D. and Senapati, S., 2008. Evening primrose oil is effective in atopic dermatitis: A randomized placebo-controlled trial. Indian Journal of Dermatology, Venereology and Leprology, 74(5), p.447.

37 Farzaneh, F., Fatehi, S., Sohrabi, M.R. and Alizadeh, K., 2013. The effect of oral evening primrose oil on menopausal hot flashes: a randomized clinical trial. Archives of gynecology and obstetrics, 288(5), pp.1075-1079.

38 De Souza, R.J., Mente, A., Maroleanu, A., Cozma, A.I., Ha, V., Kishibe, T., Uleryk, E., Budylowski, P., Schünemann, H., Beyene, J. and Anand, S.S., 2015. Intake of saturated and trans unsaturated fatty acids and risk of all cause mortality, cardiovascular disease, and type 2 diabetes: systematic review and meta-analysis of observational studies. Bmj, 351.

39 RÖSSNER, S., Von Zweigbergk, D.A.N., ÖHLIN, A. and RYTTIG, K., 1987. Weight reduction with dietary fibre supplements: results of two double-blind randomized studies. Acta Medica Scandinavica, 222(1), pp.83-88.

40 Martin, A.M., Sun, E.W., Rogers, G.B. and Keating, D.J., 2019. The influence of the gut microbiome on host metabolism through the regulation of gut hormone release. Frontiers in Physiology, 10, p.428.

41 Rose, D., Goldman, M., Connolly, J. and Strong, L., 1991. High-fiber diet reduces serum estrogen concentrations in premenopausal women. The American Journal of Clinical Nutrition, 54(3), pp.520-525.

42 Farvid, M., Spence, N., Holmes, M. and Barnett, J., 2020. Fiber consumption and breast cancer incidence: A systematic review and meta-analysis of prospective studies. Cancer, 126(13), pp.3061-3075.

43 Basu, S., Yoffe, P., Hills, N. and Lustig, R.H., 2013. The relationship of sugar to population-level diabetes prevalence: an econometric analysis of repeated cross-sectional data. PloS one, 8(2), p.e57873.

44 Messier, V., Rabasa-Lhoret, R., Barbat-Artigas, S., Elisha, B., Karelis, A.D. and Aubertin-Leheudre, M., 2011. Menopause and sarcopenia: a potential role for sex hormones. Maturitas, 68(4), pp.331-336.

45 Gregorio, L., Brindisi, J., Kleppinger, A., Sullivan, R., Mangano, K., Bihuniak, J., Kenny, A., Kerstetter, J. and Insogn, K., 2013. Adequate dietary protein is associated with better physical performance among post-menopausal women 60–90 years. The journal of nutrition, health & aging, 18(2), pp.155-160.

46 Shams-White, M., Chung, M., Du, M., Fu, Z., Insogna, K., Karlsen, M., LeBoff, M., Shapses, S., Sackey, J., Wallace, T. and Weaver, C., 2017. Dietary protein and bone health: a systematic review and meta-analysis from the National Osteoporosis Foundation. The American Journal of Clinical Nutrition, p.ajcn145110.

47 British Nutrition Foundation. 2022. Protein in a Healthy Diet. [online] Available at: https://www.nutrition.org.uk/healthy-sustainable-diets/protein/

48 Montain, S.J., Latzka, W.A. and Sawka, M.N., 1995. Control of thermoregulatory sweating is altered by hydration level and exercise intensity. Journal of Applied Physiology, 79(5), pp.1434-1439.

49 Spadola, C., Guo, N., Johnson, D., Sofer, T., Bertisch, S., Jackson, C., Rueschman, M., Mittleman, M., Wilson, J. and Redline, S., 2019. Evening intake of alcohol, caffeine, and nicotine: night-to-night associations with sleep duration and continuity among African Americans in the Jackson Heart Sleep Study. Sleep, 42(11).

50 Thurston, R.C., Ewing, L.J., Low, C.A., Christie, A.J. and Levine, M.D., 2015. Behavioral weight loss for the management of menopausal hot flashes: a pilot study. Menopause (New York, NY), 22(1), p.59.

51 Faubion, S.S., Sood, R., Thielen, J.M. and Shuster, L.T., 2015. Caffeine and menopausal symptoms: what is the association?. Menopause, 22(2), pp.155-158.

52 Harris, S.S. and Dawson-Hughes, B., 1994. Caffeine and bone loss in healthy postmenopausal women. The American journal of clinical nutrition, 60(4), pp.573-578.

53 Taneri, P.E., Kiefte-de Jong, J.C., Bramer, W.M., Daan, N.M., Franco, O.H. and Muka, T., 2016. Association of alcohol consumption with the onset of natural menopause: a systematic review and meta-analysis. Human reproduction update, 22(4), pp.516-528.

54 Dotlic, J., Markovic, N. and Gazibara, T., 2021. Patterns of smoking and menopause-specific quality of life: smoking duration matters more. Behavioral Medicine, pp.1-11.

55 Fernandez, S. and Russo, J., 2009. Estrogen and Xenoestrogens in Breast Cancer. Toxicologic Pathology, 38(1), pp.110-122.

56 Hong, A. and Kim, S., 2018. Effects of Resistance Exercise on Bone Health. Endocrinology and Metabolism, 33(4), p.435.

57 Wiklund, P., Alen, M., Munukka, E., Cheng, S.M., Yu, B., Pekkala, S. and Cheng, S., 2014. Metabolic response to 6-week aerobic exercise training and dieting in previously sedentary overweight and obese pre-menopausal women: a randomized trial. Journal of Sport and Health Science, 3(3), pp.217-224.

58 Martínez-Domínguez, S.J., Lajusticia, H., Chedraui, P., Pérez-López, F.R. and Health Outcomes and Systematic Analyses (HOUSSAY) Project, 2018. The effect of programmed exercise over anxiety symptoms in midlife and older women: a meta-analysis of randomized controlled trials. Climacteric, 21(2), pp.123-131.

59 Lee, Y. and Kim, H., 2008. Relationships between menopausal symptoms, depression, and exercise in middle-aged women: a cross-sectional survey. International journal of nursing studies, 45(12), pp.1816-1822.

60 Guthrie, J.R., Dennerstein, L. and Dudley, E.C., 1999. Weight gain and the menopause: a 5-year prospective study. Climacteric, 2(3), pp.205-211.

61 Crawford, S.L., Casey, V.A., Avis, N.E. and McKinlay, S.M., 2000. A longitudinal study of weight and the menopause transition: results from the Massachusetts Women's Health Study. Menopause (New York, NY), 7(2), pp.96-104.

62 Simkin-Silverman, L.R., Wing, R.R., Boraz, M.A. and Kuller, L.H., 2003. Lifestyle intervention can prevent weight gain during menopause: results from a 5-year randomized clinical trial. Annals of Behavioral Medicine, 26(3), pp.212-220.

63 Norton, S., Chilcot, J. and Hunter, M., 2014. Cognitive-behavior therapy for menopausal symptoms (hot flushes and night sweats). Menopause, 21(6), pp.574-578.

64 Innes, K., Selfe, T. and Vishnu, A., 2010. Mind-body therapies for menopausal symptoms: A systematic review. Maturitas, 66(2), pp.135-149.

65 Thomas, D., 2003. A Study on the Mineral Depletion of the Foods Available to us as a Nation over the Period 1940 to 1991. Nutrition and Health, 17(2), pp.85-115.

66 Sigurdsson, S., Geirsson, G., Gudmundsdottir, H., Egilsdottir, P.B. and Gudbjarnason, S., 2013. A parallel, randomized, double-blind, placebo-controlled study to investigate the effect of SagaPro on nocturia in men. Scandinavian journal of urology, 47(1), pp.26-32.

67 Kulkarni, S. and Dhir, A., 2008. Withania somnifera: An Indian ginseng. Progress in Neuro-Psychopharmacology and Biological Psychiatry, 32(5), pp.1093-1105.

68 Gopal, S., Ajgaonkar, A., Kanchi, P., Kaundinya, A., Thakare, V., Chauhan, S. and Langade, D., 2021. Effect of an ashwagandha (Withania Somnifera) root extract on climacteric symptoms in women during perimenopause: A randomized, double-blind , placebo-controlled study. Journal of Obstetrics and Gynaecology Research, 47(12), pp.4414-4425.

69 Wynn, V., 1975. Vitamins and oral contraceptive use. The Lancet, 305(7906), pp.561-564.

70 Motaghi Dastenaei, Bahareh and Safdari, Faranak and Jafarzadeh, Lobat and Raisi Dehkordi, Ziba and Taghizadeh, Mohsen and Nikzad, Maryam.,2017. The effect of Evening Primrose on hot flashes in menopausal women. The Iranian Journal of Obstetrics, Gynecology and Infertility, 20 (10). pp. 62-68.

71 Jepson, R.G. and Craig, J.C., 2007. A systematic review of the evidence for cranberries and blueberries in UTI prevention. Molecular nutrition & food research, 51(6), pp.738-745.

72 Kranjčec, B., Papeš, D. and Altarac, S., 2014. D-mannose powder for prophylaxis of recurrent urinary tract infections in women: a randomized clinical trial. World journal of urology, 32(1), pp.79-84.

73 Kuptniratsaikul, V., Dajpratham, P., Taechaarpornkul, W., Buntragulpoontawee, M., Lukkanapichonchut, P., Chootip, C., Saengsuwan, J., Tantayakom, K. and Laongpech, S., 2014. Efficacy and safety of Curcuma domestica extracts compared with ibuprofen in patients with knee osteoarthritis: a multicenter study. Clinical Interventions in Aging, 9, p.451.

74 Ataei-Almanghadim, K., Farshbaf-Khalili, A., Ostadrahimi, A.R., Shaseb, E. and Mirghafourvand, M., 2020. The effect of oral capsule of curcumin and vitamin E on the hot flashes and anxiety in postmenopausal women: A triple blind randomised controlled trial. Complementary Therapies in Medicine, 48, p.102267.

75 Stark, K., Park, E., Maines, V. and Holub, B., 2000. Effect of a fish-oil concentrate on serum lipids in postmenopausal women receiving and not receiving hormone replacement therapy in a placebo-controlled, double-blind trial. The American Journal of Clinical Nutrition, 72(2), pp.389-394.

76 De Spirt, S., Stahl, W., Tronnier, H., Sies, H., Bejot, M., Maurette, J.M. and Heinrich, U., 2008. Intervention with flaxseed and borage oil supplements modulates skin condition in women. British journal of nutrition, 101(3), pp.440-445.

77 Goldberg, R.J. and Katz, J., 2007. A meta-analysis of the analgesic effects of omega-3 polyunsaturated fatty acid supplementation for inflammatory joint pain. Pain, 129(1-2), pp.210-223.

78 Bhattacharyya, D., Sur, T.K., Jana, U. and Debnath, P.K., 2008. Controlled programmed trial of Ocimum sanctum leaf on generalized anxiety disorders. Nepal Med Coll J, 10(3), pp.176-179.

79 Erkkola, R., Vervarcke, S., Vansteelandt, S., Rompotti, P., De Keukeleire, D. and Heyerick, A., 2010. A randomized, double-blind, placebo-controlled, cross-over pilot study on the use of a standardized hop extract to alleviate menopausal discomforts. Phytomedicine, 17(6), pp.389-396.

80 Taavoni, S., Ekbatani, N., & Haghani, H., 2014. EPA-0143 – Menopausal Sleep Disorder and Use of LemonBalm: A Triple Blind Randomized Control Trial. European Psychiatry, 29(S1), 1-1

81 Brooks, N., Wilcox, G., Walker, K., Ashton, J., Cox, M. and Stojanovska, L., 2008. Beneficial effects of Lepidium meyenii (Maca) on psychological symptoms and measures of sexual dysfunction in postmenopausal women are not related to estrogen or androgen content. Menopause, 15(6), pp.1157-1162.

82 Fathizadeh, N., Ebrahimi, E., Valiani, M., Tavakoli, N., & Yar, M. H., 2010. Evaluating the effect of magnesium and magnesium plus vitamin B6 supplement on the severity of premenstrual syndrome. Iranian Journal of Nursing and Midwifery Research, 15(Suppl1), 401–405

83 Gerbarg, P.L. and Brown, R.P., 2016. Pause menopause with Rhodiola rosea, a natural selective estrogen receptor modulator. Phytomedicine, 23(7), pp.763-769.

84 Lopresti, A. and Smith, S., 2021. The Effects of a Saffron Extract (affron®) on Menopausal Symptoms in Women during Perimenopause: A Randomised, Double-Blind, Placebo-Controlled Study. Journal of Menopausal Medicine, 27(2), p.66.

85 Bommer, S., Klein, P. and Suter, A., 2011. First time proof of sage's tolerability and efficacy in menopausal women with hot flushes. Advances in Therapy, 28(6), pp.490-500.

86 Kanadys, W., Barańska, A., Błaszczuk, A., Polz-Dacewicz, M., Drop, B., Kanecki, K. and Malm, M., 2021. Evaluation of Clinical Meaningfulness of Red Clover (Trifolium pratense L.) Extract to Relieve Hot Flushes and Menopausal Symptoms in Peri- and Post-Menopausal Women: A Systematic Review and Meta-Analysis of Randomized Controlled Trials. Nutrients, 13(4), p.1258.

87 Japee, J. and Pandya, M.A., 2009. A comparative study on shatavari and kukkutanda twak bhasma in minimizing the risk of postmenopausal osteoporosis. AYU (An international quarterly journal of research in Ayurveda), 30(3), p.317.

88 Boyera, N., Galey, I. and Bernard, B.A., 1998. Effect of vitamin C and its derivatives on collagen synthesis and cross-linking by normal human fibroblasts. International journal of cosmetic science, 20(3), pp.151-158.